ORIGAMI WITH EXPLANATIONS

Fun with Folding and Math

ORIGAMI WITH EXPLANATIONS

Fun with Folding and Math

Jeanine Meyer
SUNY Purchase, USA

Takashi Mukoda

 **World Scientific**

NEW JERSEY · LONDON · SINGAPORE · BEIJING · SHANGHAI · HONG KONG · TAIPEI · CHENNAI · TOKYO

Published by

World Scientific Publishing Co. Pte. Ltd.

5 Toh Tuck Link, Singapore 596224

USA office: 27 Warren Street, Suite 401-402, Hackensack, NJ 07601

UK office: 57 Shelton Street, Covent Garden, London WC2H 9HE

Library of Congress Cataloging-in-Publication Data
Names: Meyer, Jeanine, author. | Mukoda, Takashi, author.
Title: Origami with explanations : fun with folding and math /
    Jeanine Meyer, SUNY Purchase, USA, Takashi Mukoda.
Description: New Jersey : World Scientific, [2021] | Includes index.
Identifiers: LCCN 2020042633 | ISBN 9789811220074 (hardcover) | ISBN 9789811219436 (paperback) |
    ISBN 9789811219443 (ebook for institutions) | ISBN 9789811219450 (ebook for individuals)
Subjects: LCSH: Origami. | Origami--Mathematics. | Origami in education. | Mathematics--Study and teaching.
Classification: LCC QA491 .M484 2021 | DDC 736/.982--dc23
LC record available at https://lccn.loc.gov/2020042633

British Library Cataloguing-in-Publication Data
A catalogue record for this book is available from the British Library.

Cover design by Takashi Mukoda

For any available supplementary material, please visit
https://www.worldscientific.com/worldscibooks/10.1142/11802#t=suppl

Desk Editors: Tan Rok Ting/Ramya Gangadharan

Typeset by Stallion Press
Email: enquiries@stallionpress.com

Dedication to the teachers

Lillian Oppenheimer, Michael Shall,
Laura Kruskal, Mark Kennedy

Preface

Origami, paper folding, originated hundreds of years ago in China and Japan, with independent discoveries and activities across the world. The most familiar origami models are the crane and the flapping bird. This book will introduce you to origami, starting with a jumping frog and including traditional and modern models. The models are considered simple to intermediate in complexity. We also have the goal of connecting origami and mathematics, introducing you or re-introducing you to topics such as spatial relations, geometry, algebra, and pattern finding.

Each chapter starts with the *Background* section and includes photos of the final models. When the model is not considered traditional and the designers/ inventors are known, they are credited. The authors have striven to be accurate with attributions and would appreciate any corrections and amendments.

The Instruction section has text, photos, marked up photos, and diagrams (after description of standard origami diagramming). Unlike most origami books, we do not strive for brevity, but use techniques such as providing photos with the positions of hands and fingers, and may include diagrams and photos for the same steps.

The *Explanations* section follows, in which origami and mathematics reinforce each other to provide understanding of the folding procedures. Note that we take a broad view of mathematics. Math is not limited to arithmetic calculations. There are calculations, but they are done symbolically in terms of the size of the paper and in the context of applications. Mathematics can be abstract, but here our fingers are doing the work: for example, creating a triangle that is congruent to another triangle. Calculations to determine the final dimensions of models are applications of algebra, geometry and trigonometry. The experiences in spatial relations provided by doing origami are reinforced by attention to symmetries and the transitions from 2D to 3D.

The *Enhancements and Next Steps* section provides suggestions for adding to the beauty and use of the models. It also has a preview of the next section. The *Exercises and Explorations* section offers activities for experiences building on the material in the chapter. Throughout the text, there are *Tips* for readers, parents and teachers, including suggestions on supplies. There is also an *Index*.

The material can provide an introduction to geometry, algebra and trigonometry before these topics are taught formally as well as reinforcement when the topics are part of the curriculum.

The text is suitable for individual reading as well as use in classes, home-schooling, and special programs. It will serve people with no background in origami and those who want to broaden and deepen their understanding and skill. We report that many of our students tell us that the material made them appreciate, even enjoy, math topics they had avoided in the past. They also reported enjoying time away from screens.

About the Authors

 **Jeanine Meyer** is Professor Emerita at Purchase College/ State University of New York, USA. Before moving to academia, Jeanine worked at IBM Research and other companies. She earned her PhD in Computer Science at New York University; an MA in Mathematics at Columbia University, and graduated Magna Cum Laude from the University of Chicago, majoring in Mathematics. Jeanine has authored or co-authored 8 books in computing and mathematics, plus two updates.

 **Takashi Mukoda** is a graduate of Purchase College/State University of New York, majoring both in Mathematics/ Computer Science and in New Media. He won the State University of New York Chancellor's Award and other honors. He now works as a Frontend engineer in Tokyo, Japan.

The collaboration between the two authors started with Takashi working as technical reviewer for three of Jeanine's books on programming. Takashi contributed to the design of the Purchase College general education course on origami and mathematics before the start of the course and was one of the class teaching assistants for the first class in Spring 2019. Jeanine recruited him to be co-author after his return to Japan.

Acknowledgments

We acknowledge the work of Lillian Oppenheimer, Sam Ciulla, Laura Kruskal, Peter Engel, Junior Fritz Jacquet, Tomoko Fuse, Gay Merrill Gross, Robert Neale, Martin Kruskal, Phillip Shen, Paul Jackson, and David Mitchell, and thank them along with family members Kish Shen and Karen Kruskal and Clyde Kruskal for granting us permission to feature their work in our books.

We also want to acknowledge and thank readers and people who gave us advice and encouragement: Gay Merrill Gross, Robert Lang, Jeremy Shafer, David Brill, David Mitchell, Rona Gurkewitz, Julianna Biro, Jan Polish (of OrigamiUSA), Gilad Aharoni (Gilad's List), Dr. Florence Mann, Alexander Kellerman, Joey Kellerman, Nico Kellerman and others. They are not responsible for any mistakes.

We want to thank Purchase College/SUNY colleagues Knarik Tunyan and Irina Shablinsky, for suggesting we conduct the origami mathematics general education class and their considerable help to us both over the years.

Contents

Chapter 1

Magazine Cover Box and Business Card Frog

Background

Picking the first origami model to teach or to learn is a frequent topic of conversation among paper folders. Jeanine's first exposure to origami was the Flapping Bird (see Chapter 6) featured in the *Mathematical Games* section of **Scientific American**. It is a beautiful model and it and/or the crane, a related model, are used to represent origami. Jeanine enjoyed making the model but did not pursue any more origami. Years later she was fortunate to be among the very large number of people who received personal instruction from Lillian Oppenheimer, the person credited with helping to popularize origami in the United States. Lillian Oppenheimer founded The Origami Center of America in 1958, now known as OrigamiUSA. She taught Jeanine the Business Card Frog, shown in Figure 1.1. Stroking the back of the model as shown will make the frog jump.

Figure 1.1.   Business Card Frog.

Lillian said that she taught this model to Japanese businessmen, telling them that if they did it, people would not throw away their business cards. By the way, she did not believe that people should start with the flapping bird because it is too challenging for beginners. Our experience supports Lillian. We have found the Business Card Frog model to be extremely useful for entertaining children (and children of all ages), such as when waiting on line or even in Emergency waiting rooms.

This frog is an *action model* and needs something to jump into, so we will start with the Magazine Cover Box, shown in Figure 1.2.

Figure 1.2.   Magazine Cover Box.

Instructions

Magazine Cover Box

We suggest doing this model first with ordinary printer/copier paper. Using actual magazine covers will come later. In the USA, "ordinary paper" means 8.5 × 11 inches. Alternatively, A4 paper (210 × 270 millimeters) also would do: the critical factor is that it is a rectangle that is not a square. This means that the angles are right angles and opposite sides are the same length but there are long sides and short sides.

    Fold a long side to the opposite side, making a fold line in the middle, dividing the paper into two equal parts. Now unfold. You have made what is called a *book fold* as shown in Figure 1.3.

Figure 1.3. Book fold.

If you take both edges and open and close this fold, it is like opening a book. You have also made a *valley fold*. Pick up the paper and hold it partially unfolded (and balanced on a table) and you will see a V as shown in Figure 1.4.

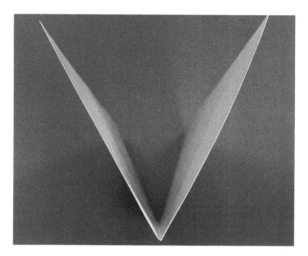

Figure 1.4.   Book fold showing V shape.

If you turn the paper over, the upside-down V shape looks like a peak, which is called a *mountain fold*. When you make a valley fold, you are always making a mountain fold on the other side, or vice versa. From the valley fold side, the crease forms a groove. From the mountain fold side, the crease forms a peak that you can pinch.

The crease from the book fold is visible and it will be used for the next two steps. Take each long edge, also called *cut edge*, and fold it to the book fold crease and then unfold. Figure 1.5 shows the results: three creases on the paper. We have put in lines so you can see the folds.

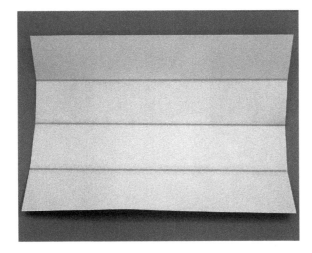

Figure 1.5.   Paper showing results of book fold and cupboard folds.

These two steps are called *cupboard folds*. Opening and closing these folds is like opening and closing a cupboard. Yes, we are folding and unfolding. We are making progress.

Each of the two cupboard folds divides half of the paper in half again. This produces quarter folds. That is, there are four rectangles and the width of each is one-quarter the width of the paper. One quarter, or 1/4, means that each section is one part of four.

With the paper completely unfolded, we will repeat what we just did, but now short side to short side: first make a book fold: the short edge to the opposite edge. Unfold and then each short edge to the book fold line just made. This time do not unfold the cupboard folds. Figure 1.6 shows the model so far.

Figure 1.6.   Results of folding each short edge to the book fold line.

Following the model of a master teacher, Michael Shall, this is where we shout, "Hands in lap!" The intent is to warn you that the next step is a little tricky or has the possibility of misinterpretation, so you need to listen to (or see) all the instructions before continuing.

Take a corner point (any of the four corners will do to start because you will do the same operation to all the corners). Fold it so that the edge aligns with the nearest crease line in the paper. For guidance, look ahead to Figure 1.7. Reinforce this fold, meaning go over it with your fingers. There are products called *bone folders* for reinforcing folds. Tongue depressors, credit cards, and used gift cards are also good for reinforcing folds and making sharp creases is important.

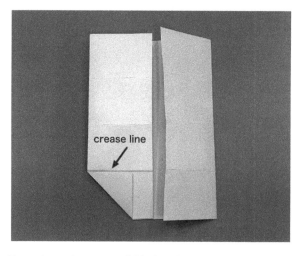

Figure 1.7.   One corner folded to align with the crease line.

Notice that the bottom cut edges when folded do not line up with the center. There is some extra paper, which we can call a margin or a lip or a (potential) hem. This will used for a lock, but you need to be patient. Make sure your model looks like Figure 1.7.

Repeat the folding up of the corners three more times. You treat each corner the same. This model has symmetry, namely bilateral symmetry in both dimensions. Bilateral symmetry is a property that two identical parts face each other around an axis. This formal, mathematical term is appropriate here and will help you learn and then recall the folding sequence. It means that the sides match up both vertically, using a line dividing the model in two from top to bottom, and horizontally, using a line going left to right. Look at Figure 1.8 and compare with your model.

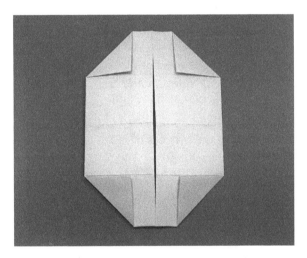

Figure 1.8.   All four corners folded to align with crease lines.

Now, we use the margin/lip/hem material on each side and fold it over the corner folds. It may be easier to orient the paper so that the slit is horizontal. This is two operations, one for each side: each hem will lie on top of 2 corner folds, as shown in Figure 1.9. Be careful and it helps to start from the middle because the paper can tear (but if it does, keep going and remember it is only paper!).

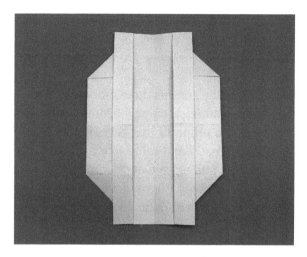

Figure 1.9.   Hem made over corner folds.

The paper is now a funny shape—not a mathematical term—being close to an octagon, but actually with 12 sides. In any case, keep going.

One more step: grab one folded hem with each hand and bring it up and out to create a 3D shape. It is helpful to reinforce the edges to each corner. Figure 1.10 shows the start of the process of reaching in and separating the edges to make the model three dimensional.

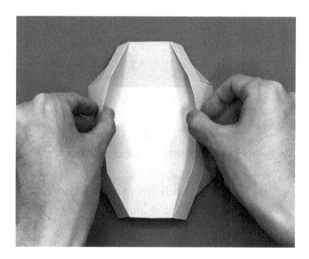

Figure 1.10.   Starting making the model 3D.

Figure 1.11. Finish shaping the box.

You have a box! See Figures 1.11 and 1.12.

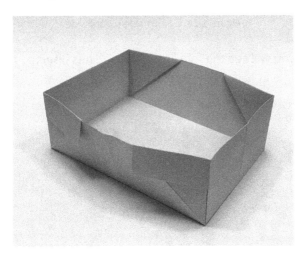

Figure 1.12. Finished box.

Business Card Frog

The Business Card Frog also is made with a rectangle that is not a square. For this model, the paper should be somewhat stiff. A business card satisfies those requirements, as does an index card. Starting with bigger paper the first time you attempt to make an origami model is generally a good idea, so consider starting with a 3 × 5 index card if one is available.

Take a short side and fold it to align with an adjacent long side. You are pivoting on a corner. I have used an index card with wiggly lines on the back side (to distinguish from the front side). See Figure 1.13.

Figure 1.13.   Short side to long side.

Unfold and you will see the fold line just made has bisected the angle; that is, it divided the angle in half. See Figure 1.14.

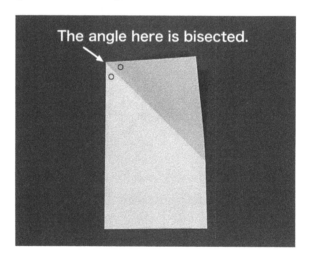

Figure 1.14.   Valley fold bisecting the angle.

Do the same thing but this time fold the top, short edge to the other long edge (that is, if you folded to the left long side first, now fold to the right long side). See Figure 1.15.

Figure 1.15. Top, short side to other long side.

Unfold. Figure 1.16 shows an X made by valley folds.

Figure 1.16. Paper showing X of valley folds.

Now turn the paper over. You will see an X made of mountain folds as shown in Figure 1.17.

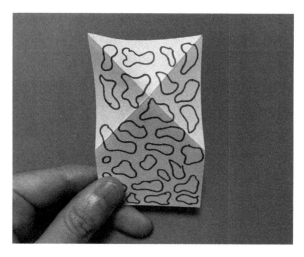

Figure 1.17.   Now showing X of mountain folds.

Unless you push down on the paper, it resembles a tent. Now take the top edge and fold it to the ends of the X, making a fold that goes through the crossing point of the X. Figure 1.18 shows the last fold covering up the X.

Figure 1.18.   Showing top edge to bottom of X.

Now unfold and you will see something like Figure 1.19.

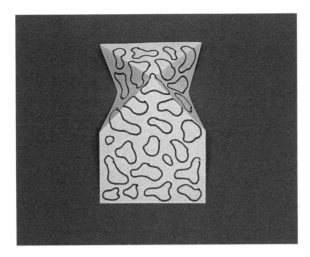

Figure 1.19. Model again has a tent-like shape.

Press the sides in to collapse the model into an arrow-head, as shown in Figures 1.20 and 1.21.

Figure 1.20. Tent collapsed into arrow head shape.

Figure 1.21. Done collapsing the model.

In most origami, folds are made to definite targets, also called *landmarks*; fold an edge to another edge or a point to a point. We also reinforce folds, saying "no wimpy folds." So far in the Business Card Frog Procedure we have needed very strong folds, but later this model has steps that do not follow these rules.

Turn the model over and fold up one of the points towards the top point, but not all the way, as shown in Figure 1.22. This is called a "to taste fold." This is the first of the two front legs of the frog. Repeated experience folding this model will tell you where you like the legs to appear, and how far to fold to get there.

Figure 1.22. One leg up.

Fold up the other leg to match. See Figure 1.23.

Figure 1.23.   Two legs formed.

Now *skinny* the model: take each side, and fold it towards the center of the model. That is, you take the cut, raw edge and make a folded edge. This is another to taste fold. Again, you can try to maintain the symmetry. An alternate approach is to make the legs folded up to the center and then make the sides fold all the way to the center. You decide. See Figure 1.24.

Figure 1.24.   Both sides in to skinny model.

Two more folds and we are done. Usually, when making a fold, you want to break the fibers in the paper. Unlike the prior folds, these two folds should NOT be reinforced, that is, leave them soft and rounded. This often is called *wimpy*! Fold the bottom to the top. Takashi does this over his fingers as shown in Figure 1.25.

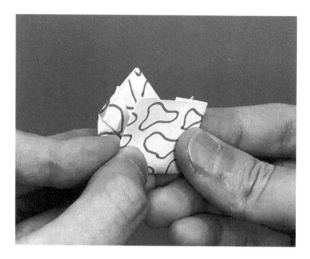

Figure 1.25.   Bottom to top.

Now take what is now at the top and fold it back on itself to the fold line just made as shown in Figure 1.26.

Figure 1.26.   Fold paper back to fold just made.

Turn the model over and place on a flat surface. What do you do with this highly stylized, frog-looking shape? Slide your finger down the head/back (gently) and release to make the frog jump as shown in Figure 1.27.

Figure 1.27.　Making the frog jump.

Where should it jump? Into the box.

Explanations

Magazine Cover Box

Many origami models have a step (or steps) that produces an arrangement of the paper that locks the model together and, in many cases, allows it to take a three dimensional shape. For the Magazine Cover Box, this is the step when we fold what I termed the margin/lip/hem over the folded corners. The completion of the locking operation is shown in Figure 1.9 and the start of the transition to 3D is shown in Figure 1.10.

The hem material of the paper exists because the paper is a rectangle and not a square. How big is it? That is, what is the width of the hem? Look at Figure 1.8

before the fold of the hem. Going back in the folding process, folding long edge to long edge produced a line in the middle, forming two rectangular areas. The vertical length of each of these areas is the same as the long edge. The width is half the length of the short edge.

Continuing with the analysis, making cupboard folds produces long, skinny rectangles, with length again the original length and width half of the half, which is one-quarter of the original width. Folding the short side to short side produces two rectangles each with one dimension the original width and the other half the original length. Folding the cupboard fold does a similar halving of the half.

Here is where using letters for numbers makes things easy. If the original dimensions are w by h, using copier paper, w is 8.5 and h is 11, but let's sticks with w and h. In Figure 1.28, you see labeling indicating the lengths of the small rectangles in terms of the original orientation of the paper, with w referring to the short side and h referring to the long side.

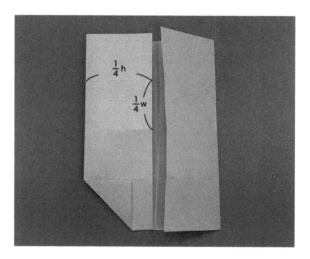

Figure 1.28.   Labels indicating width and height.

The width of the hem is

$$\frac{h}{4} - \frac{w}{4}.$$

This is equivalent to 1/4 times (h − w).

$$\frac{1}{4}(h-w).$$

To say it in English, the width of the lock is one-fourth of the difference between the long side and the short side. But, why? There is a triangle on the bottom left. Because the length of its top and right edges are the same, the top edge is w/4. That is why it is possible to get the width of the hem by subtracting w/4 from h/4.

Using the symbols, w and h, are easier to work with and tell a better story. For copier/printer paper, the difference is 11 − 8.5 so the hem would measure one-fourth of 2.5 inches.

There are many origami boxes. For example, we describe what is called a Masu box in our book, **More Origami with Explanations**. The Magazine Cover box has features that can be considered good and not-so-good. It is very flexible, so you can make a second box with exactly the same paper and use it for a lid. However, this lack of rigidity means that the box is pretty flimsy. Its thickness is mostly just one layer of paper. For the Masu box, you will observe that the sides and bottom are at least two layers of paper thick.

Business Card Frog

To compute the final dimensions of the frog, we need to provide ranges or be more specific about the to-taste folds. We'll ignore the positioning of the front legs, but we can calculate the length of the legs.

Unfolding the model (which we urge you to do), you see Figure 1.29. The A and B labels indicate the extent of one of the frog's legs.

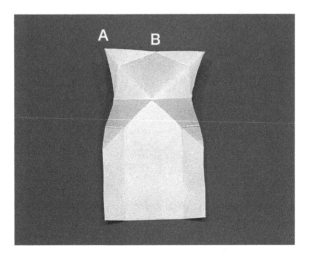

Figure 1.29. Unfolded model.

As you can see from the marked photo, the segment AB is one half the width of the model.

To make a calculation of the width of the frog model, we need to provide a range or be specific about the step to skinny the model. Let's say that we fold the edges all the way to the center, like cupboard folds. Then the width of the frog is one-half the width of the original paper.

We describe a frog study in the exercises.

Enhancements and Next Steps

Many models can benefit from doing some refinements. How about using an actual magazine cover for the Magazine Cover Box? There are two matters that are important here in terms of the look of the final model. One is the matter of some extra folds and the other concerns your choice of where the picture on the cover is to appear.

If you examine the box, notice that there are fold lines that do not appear to be used. See Figure 1.30. Take a moment to see if you can figure out when these folds were made. You can flatten the box and then take it apart.

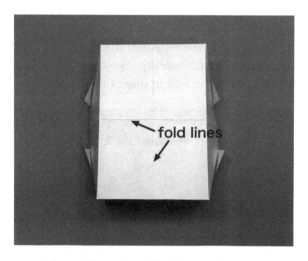

Figure 1.30.   View of box from underneath.

You will see that these folds arise from the original long edge to long edge and short edge to short edge book folds. These are not folded in the final model, but the crease lines were used as landmarks, namely targets in making the cupboard folds. What can we do to serve this purpose without making folds? The answer is to line up the edges as you begin to make the book folds, but make what are termed *pinches* on the sides instead of making a complete crease, as shown in Figure 1.31.

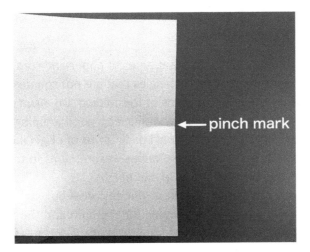

Figure 1.31.   Paper showing one of the pinch marks.

These pinch marks are enough to define the positioning of the cupboard folds and they are not prominent in the final model.

Another consideration for your enhanced box is that you need to decide what is on the inside of the box and what is on the outside.

You can work this out "in your head," but another approach is to take a finished box, put a mark in the inside, and take the box apart so it is a more or less flat piece of paper. Where is your mark? The mark is on the side facing up when you/we started making the book folds and, in fact, all of the folding.

The Magazine Cover Box did not have any flipping over of the paper. Recall that the Business Card Frog did, and this will be the case for many models in this book.

There is a Business Card Bunny designed by Gay Merrill Gross, that is similar to the frog. The front legs are not folded and, instead, the flaps are lifted to represent ears, and the last two folds are on the underside.

You also will find discussion of the traditional frog in this book and many more frogs online. There will be an exercise to do the research to find out why there are so many origami frogs.

Chapter 2 features two more traditional models: Fluttering Butterfly, which has just four folds, and Star Basket. There will be more frogs and more boxes in later chapters. There also will be an introduction to origami diagramming, though we still will make use of photographs in situations when we believe it helps your understanding.

Exercises and Explorations

1. Frog jumping study: collect different types of paper and compare for jumping ability. The papers must all be rectangles that are not squares. You do need to be consistent on the last two steps of the folding. Do also consider different sizes of the same type of paper. What makes a good jumping frog?
2. Compute the dimensions of the final box in terms of original dimensions w by h. The dimensions consist of three values—expressions in terms of w and h. These are the two sides of the base and height.
3. Make box from paper with different dimensions—but still a rectangle that isn't a square—and apply the formula for the hem and the final dimensions and make actual measurements to confirm that the formulas are correct.
4. Experiment: can the margin be too big? Can it be too little?
5. Look up the Business Card Bunny (designed by Gay Merrill Gross) or experiment yourself, and make it. Compare with the Business Card Frog.
6. Compare the symmetries of the Business Card Frog and the Magazine Cover Box. Assume all the "to taste" folds in the Frog are matched. Hint: they are not the same.
7. It is true that you can use the same size box to serve as a lid because of the flexibility. How could you make a slightly bigger box?

Chapter 2

Fluttering Butterfly and Star Basket

Background

The models in this chapter are made from square paper. The first model in this chapter, the Fluttering Butterfly (sometimes called the Wiggler), takes just four folds. We could not determine its inventor and would appreciate any leads. It is a fun, action model, shown in Figure 2.1.

Figure 2.1. Fluttering Butterfly.

The second model, the Star Basket, is considered traditional (see Figure 2.2). It is a nice container for candy. You can decorate it and make variations. We will show how to calculate the size of the bottom. The Star Basket starts with one of what are called *origami bases*. A base is a set of folds that is the start of many models. This base has two names: *preliminary base* or *square base*.

Figure 2.2.   Star Basket.

We will introduce origami diagrams in this chapter. The modern approach to diagramming was introduced by Akira Yoshizawa. Samuel Randlett and Robert Harbin made contributions. The diagramming method was first published in a non-Japanese book, in Randlett's classic book, *Art of Origami*, in 1961. Diagramming is now an international standard.

SUPPLIES

Fluttering Butterfly

Square paper. The standard origami paper is called *kami*, the Japanese word for paper. It is thinner than copier paper, which has advantages for folding. The most common type is white on one side and a solid color or a pattern on the other. The so-called duo paper has a different color on each side, neither white. The Fluttering Butterfly can be made with 5 or 6-inch.

Star Basket

Square paper. Consider using bigger paper, say 10-inch for the Star Basket. The Star Basket is worthy of pretty paper, such as one with an elaborate design, since it is suitable for a gift. However, for your first practice model, it makes sense to use plain (no design), light colored paper. This helps you see the crease marks.

Instructions

Fluttering Butterfly

Orient the square paper so that it is a diamond, with one of the corners pointing at you! Fold the bottom corner to the top corner. The mathematical term for a corner is *vertex*, plural form *vertices*.

TIP

It helps with neatness to line up the top corners to match first, and crease from the center out to each side (rather than lining up the side corners and folding straight across). There are lots of little tricks for folding neatly and cleanly, but, in general, skilled origami is achieved by folding slowly and deliberately and improved by repeated practice. Folding is not a race (unless you are in an origami convention novelty competition such as folding behind your back as quickly as you can!).

This fold is called a *diagonal fold* or a *diaper fold* (after old-fashioned cloth diapers). Figure 2.3 shows fold types and their corresponding line styles.

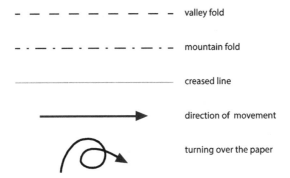

valley fold

mountain fold

creased line

direction of movement

turning over the paper

Figure 2.3. Fold types and their corresponding line styles.

In Figure 2.4, you see the diamond shape and a dashed line across the middle. The dashed line represents a valley fold. Mountain folds are depicted with dots and dashes. Each diagram shows the state of the model and, in most cases, the fold you are instructed to make *next*. Any crease lines produced by past steps generally (though not always) are depicted by light-weight lines.

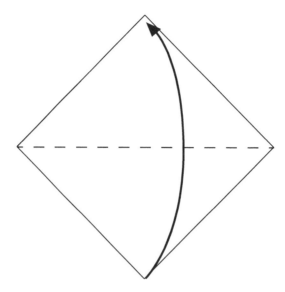

Figure 2.4.   Instruction for diagonal fold.

Figure 2.5 shows a triangle. It is the result of the previous fold. The point at the top represents one corner lying on top of another. We will call this point in our diagram a vertex and note that it is 90 degrees, so the triangle is a right triangle. The triangle also is an *isosceles triangle*, meaning two sides have equal length and this is important. Now there is a new dashed line down the middle. This indicates the next fold to make.

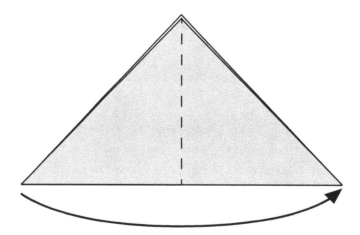

Figure 2.5.   Ready for second fold.

The results of the first two folds are shown in Figure 2.6. The paper is now a different triangle. The exact positioning of the next fold: a vertical valley fold is called "to taste." Sometimes such folds are called *R.A.T. folds*, an acronym for Right-About-There. One way to make this fold, and the way Jeanine was taught, is to put your finger next to the fold line just made and fold one layer to the left, over your finger, and then pull out your finger and flatten the paper.

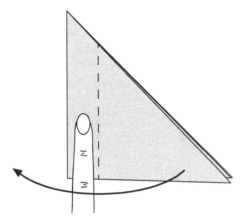

Figure 2.6. Ready for the third step, fold one layer to the left.

Figure 2.7 shows the result of the third fold. The next step is to turn the model over. That is, pick it up off the table, turn it over, and put it down. Origami diagrams usually show this with an arrow that has a loop in the middle.

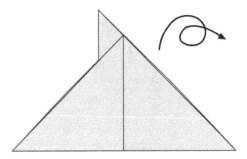

Figure 2.7. Result of the third fold.

The result of turning the model over is shown in Figure 2.8. The fourth and last fold is to fold the flap on top to the right to match the flap already made that is now on the bottom. The fold line is given but the way to do it is to match up the flaps, now on the right.

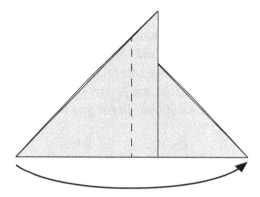

Figure 2.8.   Indicates fourth fold: fold flap to right, matching the other flap underneath.

The results of the four folds are shown in Figure 2.9. The Fluttering Butterfly is on its side.

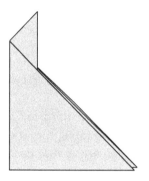

Figure 2.9.   Results of the four folds.

Now pick up the model and place it as shown back in Figure 2.10 and tap the spine to see the wings flutter.

Figure 2.10. Demonstrate how to flutter the wings.

Star Basket

The Star Basket, in addition to its practical uses, provides a start to the discussion of origami bases. To repeat: an origami base is a set of folds that is the start of many models. The bases for Star Basket has two names: *preliminary base* and *square base*. It also has an intriguing relationship to the *waterbomb base*, which you will see in the next chapter.

White side up, fold bottom edge to top edge. This is what we called a book fold in Chapter 1 (see Figure 2.11).

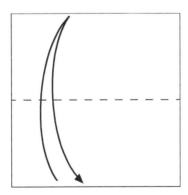

Figure 2.11. Make book fold and unfold.

Figure 2.12 shows that the prior fold is indicated by a thin line. The next fold is another fold edge to opposite edge. It is indicated by a dashed, vertical line.

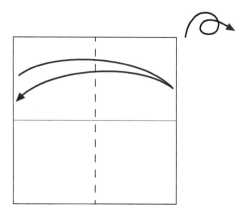

Figure 2.12.   Make second book fold and unfold and turn over.

Of course, you can make these folds going from top to bottom; rotate and then bottom to top again, or any way you want. The objective is to produce two creases. Each divides the paper in half, so after folding and unfolding both, both together divide the paper into four parts of equal area. Turn the paper over and the color side is now up. Orient the paper into a diamond shape. This is to make your paper correspond to our directions.

Now make a diagonal fold, that is, bottom corner to top corner. Figure 2.13 shows that the two book folds are indicated by thin lines. The next fold is indicated by a dashed line going from corner to opposite corner.

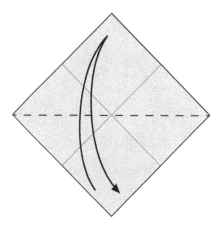

Figure 2.13.   Make one diagonal.

Unfold and repeat with the other diagonal fold (see Figure 2.14). Notice that the thin lines are representing the previous book folds and the first diagonal fold.

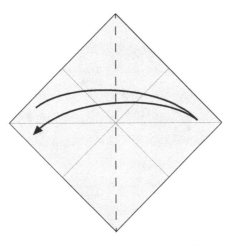

Figure 2.14.   Make second diagonal fold.

Unfold. Now, you may recall the start of the Business Card Frog. We collapsed the model into an arrow. We do a similar thing now. This step will produce the base called by two names: *preliminary* and *square*. It is preliminary to the *bird base* that you will read about in Chapter 6. It is called the square base because it does produce a square. The photos in Figures 2.15 and 2.16 show the model in two configurations. In Figure 2.15, the center is higher than the rest and in Figure 2.16, it is lower. We want the center higher, the tent-like configuration, so pop the center up to achieve that if it is not what you have in your model.

Figure 2.15.   Tent-like, center high, configuration.

Figure 2.16.   Punched down paper.

Push in on the diagonal fold just made and grab two opposing rib-like folds that arose from the book folds and press together to form the square base. Figures 2.17 and 2.18 show the process.

Figure 2.17.   Press the book folds.

Figure 2.18. Square base.

If you have the center-down configuration and squeeze the left and right squares and push, you will get a triangle shaped result, which resembles the arrowhead in the Business Card fold. This is called the *waterbomb base* and you will see it in the next chapter.

TIP

Up until the collapse, the waterbomb base and the square base are made by the same folds! Of course, it does make a difference starting with the white side up or the color side up. To make a square base with the color on the outside, you start as described here: book folds starting with white side up. To make a waterbomb (triangle) base with the color on the outside, start with diagonal folds with the white side up. In each case, to make the base with the color on this inside, you start the opposite way and some models do require this. Practice making them and observe how the creases and the edges move. See the Exercises for challenges.

Back to the square base: The model is now one-quarter of the size of the original square piece of paper. (The diagrams and photos may not be to scale. You will see zooming to show more detail in origami directions.) The square base has four flaps. Orient it so that the closed point is at the top and the cut edges are at the bottom and two flaps are on each side (see Figure 2.19). You will perform the next steps on each of the four flaps.

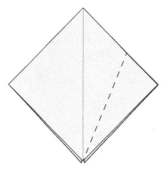

Figure 2.19.   This square base drawing indicates the next fold, a preparation fold.

The fold indicated by the dashed lines is what is called a *preparation fold*. In this case, it is preparation for a *squash fold*. People doing diagrams may convey a squash fold in different ways. We will use photos here. Make the preparation fold, which aligns two layers of paper, a double cut edge, to the center line. Press very firmly and then partially unfold the fold just made (see Figure 2.20).

Figure 2.20.   Partially unfold preparation fold.

Put your finger in between the two layers to separate the layers as indicated in Figure 2.21.

Figure 2.21. Separate the layers.

Now slide your finger inside the pocket, to the top of the pocket to open it up. Remove your finger and press (squash) down keeping the sides of the pocket symmetric, to get what is shown in Figure 2.22.

Figure 2.22. Completed squash fold.

Move the whole flap over to the left. Turn the model over and move a flap to the other side so you still have two flaps on each side. Keeping the flaps balanced, so to speak, will make the folding easier. Turn the model back over. This turning of the pages (one on the front and one on the back) is called a *minor miracle*. (It is meant to be ironic.) Repeat the same sequence with all the flaps: make a preparation fold, partially unfold and make a squash fold. You will need to turn the model over for four squash folds in all. It will look like what is shown in Figure 2.23.

Figure 2.23.   After all four squash folds.

If you pick up the model, separate the four flaps, and look down at the closed point, you see what is shown in Figure 2.24. The model has what is termed *radial symmetry*.

Figure 2.24.   Looking at model from above closed top.

Lay the model down again.

The next set of steps is to wrap half of each squash fold back on itself. We hope it is not a surprise that we will be doing the wrap operation four times. Each kite-shaped squash fold is mountain-folded in half. Figure 2.25 shows this in progress.

Figure 2.25. Start of wrap operation.

Notice that the new fold line is a mountain fold when facing this direction. Figure 2.26 shows two wrapping operations complete on the right side.

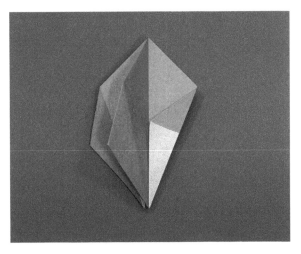

Figure 2.26. Shows wrap complete on the right.

Look at the left side of the model. You see a mountain fold, which marks the back of half of a squash fold. Make the mountain fold into a valley by folding half of that squash fold. This is the third wrap operation. The result is shown in Figure 2.27.

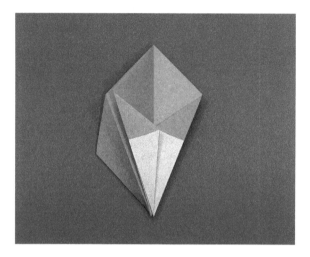

Figure 2.27.   Showing two wraps complete on one side.

Turn the model over and do one more wrap around step. You will produce what is shown in Figure 2.28. The front and the back look the same.

Figure 2.28.   Wraps complete.

The model has four long flaps at the bottom.

Take each of the flaps and fold them up. The valley fold line shown in Figure 2.29 is at the highest point that you can easily make the fold. Unfold and repeat behind. Do a minor miracle and fold two flaps up and down. The same instruction is shown in the diagram in Figure 2.30.

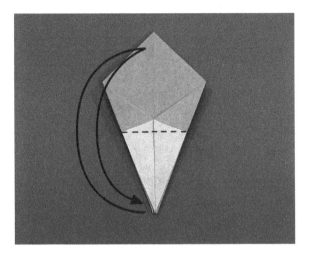

Figure 2.29.   Showing the next step, fold up the flap up and unfold.

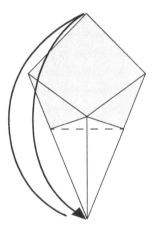

Figure 2.30.   Fold point up.

You can jump immediately to making the model three dimensional or make preparation folds as indicated in Figures 2.31 (hybrid photo/diagram) and 2.32 (diagram) to form the base. You can do this step two times, once on the front and turn the model over and repeat or do minor miracles and repeat the step two more times. The base will be a square and the preparation folds shape the four sides of the square.

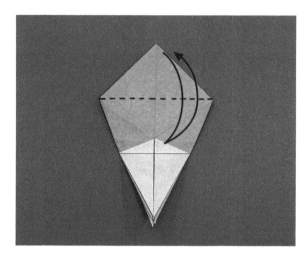

Figure 2.31.   Preparation folds for the base.

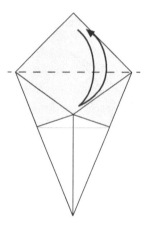

Figure 2.32.   Prepare base.

The reason NOT to make these preparation folds is to make the base have a soft curve.

Form the model by pulling on the four flaps and poking your fingers inside to shape the base. Figures 2.33 and 2.34 show how to transform the model into a box.

Figure 2.33. Pulling out the four flaps.

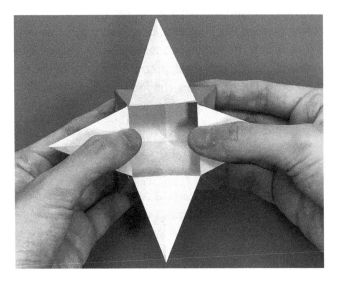

Figure 2.34. Flatten the base.

See Figure 2.35 for what the model should look like.

Figure 2.35.   Complete Star Basket.

Do make the model again, perhaps with pretty paper. Do keep in mind that though it may have seemed like a lot of folding, many steps were performed four times. We can summarize the folding: square base, four squash folds, four wrap folds, four flaps folded up and unfolded, prepare the base of the model, make the model three dimensional by separating the four flaps, opening the container, and forming the model.

TIP

Most origami books have just photos or just diagrams and they tend to have little or no text instruction for each step. At some point, you may come to like the brevity. In any case, learning how to read diagrams will help you learn models outside of reading this book. If you find videos giving instructions—and there are very good videos, though also mediocre ones—you can sketch diagrams and use origami and mathematical language when making notes to remember what you saw.

Explanations

The Fluttering Butterfly flutters because of the effects of the zig-zag folds. The folds act as a spring and the spring produces the flutter. It is similar to the way that pressing on the Business Card Frog causes the folds to act as a spring and make the frog jump.

A squash fold is done on a part of the paper that has at least two layers. The preparation fold makes creases on both layers. Making the squash unfolds one crease while maintaining the sense of the other. The squash also adds folds.

We now describe the calculation of the side of the base of the Star Basket in terms of the length of the side of the original square paper. The calculation will be done using concepts from geometry and trigonometry.

About Geometry and Trigonometry

You can skip this section and come back to it when you feel the need, for example when using the terms in calculating the size of the base of the Star Basket.

Geometry, trigonometry, algebra, etc. gain their power from being abstract. Geometry is concerned with the abstractions of shapes, such as rectangles and squares and triangles. These entities only exist as represented on paper and in our minds. Origami, in contrast, deals with actual pieces of paper. The folding creates [crease] lines on the paper, including ones forming squares, triangles and other shapes.

Congruent and Similar

In mathematics, triangles are defined to be enclosed shapes, with three straight sides. The sides meet at points (aka vertices) and define angles. The sides and the angles can be measured. Using the degree measurement system, the sum of the measurements of the three angles is 180 degrees. A *right triangle* has one angle that is 90 degrees and two other angles that add up to 90 degrees. Another way to describe the two lines that meet at a right angle is to say that the lines are *perpendicular*. The typical practice in origami is *not* to get out a ruler or a protractor but to form shapes by creasing the paper using edges, creases and points as landmarks.

Two concepts frequently appear in proofs and calculations concerning triangles: two triangles can be described as being *congruent* or two triangles can be described as being *similar*.

Two triangles are said to be *congruent* if the sides and angles are the same, that is, they match up. Using English, congruent triangles are the same shape and size. There are rules that can be applied to determine congruency. Using origami, being congruent is much more immediate, physical, concrete, and, often, obvious. For example, two triangles are congruent because an edge was folded over so that one triangle defined and lay on top of a second triangle. Your folding does the proof.

Two triangles are *similar* in mathematics if the angles are the same. The mathematical definition is precise but certainly related to the meaning of the English word.

Figure 2.36 shows two triangles that are a special type called right triangles.

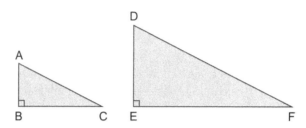

Figure 2.36.   Similar right triangles.

We could use the word similar in its ordinary English meaning when describing these triangles. We also might say they are the same shape. Assuming our coding was correct when we wrote the program to produce these drawings, the angles all match: the angle at A is the same as the angle at D; the angle at B is the same as the angle at E; the angle at C is the same as the angle at F. The mathematical concept of triangles being similar saves us a lot of words!

If two triangles are similar, then statements can be made about the sides. Corresponding sides of similar triangles, say AB and DE in Figure 2.36, may not be the same length, but the ratios of lengths of one side to another in the triangle *are* the same. The ratio of the length AB to the length AC is the same as the ratio of the length DE to the length DF. The ratio of the length BC to the length AC is the same as the ratio of the length EF to the length DF. Use your finger and point to the edges while re-reading this paragraph.

We can make a different set of statements. The ratio of the length AB to the length DE is the same as the ratio of AC to DF. All this follows from the triangles being similar. Folding can create similar triangles. Speaking more generally, people doing origami experience similarity all the time: we fold models from different sizes of paper, using the same sequence of steps.

Trigonometry

Trigonometry is based on right triangles. If you take a square piece of paper and make a diagonal fold, you produce a right triangle. In this case, two of the sides are the same length. If you take a rectangle that is NOT a square and make a crease from point to opposite point, you will produce two right triangles that have two sides ending at the right angle that are NOT the same size. Trig facts work "in the other direction": if the lengths of two sides have a certain ratio, then the angles are determined. See Fact #3 below. You will see this in action in this book and our second book, *More Origami with Explanations*. The ratios of the sides have names (for example, sine and cosine) but the concept is more important than the terminology. (We do find them useful for programming work or for crossword puzzles.)

In proving facts and making calculations about origami models, we use what we know from the folding steps and facts about triangles and other shapes. Here are three facts that we will use in this chapter and others.

Fact #1. The *Pythagoras Theorem* states that if the sides of a right triangle measure a, b, and c (Figure 2.37), with c the length of the side opposite the right angle, named the *hypotenuse*, then

$$a^2 + b^2 = c^2$$

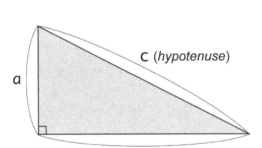

Figure 2.37. Right Triangle.

We probably will only use one specific application of this rule, but it is an important one. *The length of the diagonal of a square (piece of paper) is the length of the side times the square root of 2 (=√2).* We now describe how to arrive at this calculation. We use *x* as something to be calculated. (Don't be scared.) So, if we start with a square, when we fold the paper in half along the diagonal, we produce a right triangle with two equal sides. If is the size of the side of the square, then Pythagoras Theorem says, since $a = b = s$,

$$s \times s + s \times s = x \times x$$

Doing a little algebra,

$$2 \times s \times s = x \times x$$

Taking the square root of both sides

$$\sqrt{2} \times s = x$$

So, the length of the diagonal is the length of the side times √2. This is true for ALL squares. If we actually needed to know what this was, we would use a calculator or our computer.

Fact #2. If two angles of a triangle measure the same, the sides opposite those angles are the same length. This is called an *isosceles* triangle (from the Greek, *iso* means equal and *skeles* refers to legs or, in this situation, sides). If one of the angles in a right triangle is 45 degrees (half of 90 degrees), then so is the other angle that is NOT the right angle. The two sides coming out from the right angle are the same length. The angles are 90, 45 and 45 (Figure 2.38). This is because the sum of all the angles must be 180 degrees.

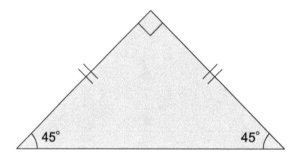

Figure 2.38. 45–45–90 isosceles triangle.

Fact #3. If one of the angles of a triangle is 30 degrees, then *the ratio of the side opposite that angle to the side opposite the right angle is one half*. Now, let's say we don't know the angles except that the triangle is a right triangle. If we do know that the ratio of the shortest side to the hypotenuse (the side opposite the right angle) is 1/2, then the angles of this triangle are 30, 60 and 90 degrees. The triangle in Figure 2.39 is a 30–60–90 triangle.

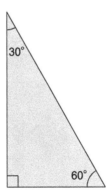

Figure 2.39. 30–60–90 right triangle.

We can go far with just this background.

Size of Star Basket base

Please do the following with a Star Basket. (This is not the model you made out of pretty paper to give as a gift.) Take a pen, reach inside and outline the base. Then take the model apart. You should see something like Figure 2.40.

Figure 2.40. Unfolded, marked model.

Now, we want you to focus on just one quarter of the paper, the lower left quarter. Examine the diagram and the photo in Figure 2.41. This represents the fold lines after the square base is made and the preparation fold for the squash fold made and then unfolded. This fold made edge CD line up with diagonal CB and defined the point H. Look at both figures until you are comfortable that the labeled diagram does represent the model. Line FG represents a side of the base of the Star Basket and all the sides are the same length.

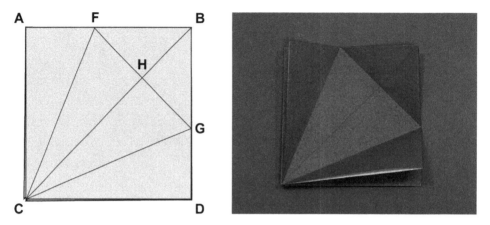

Figure 2.41.   One-quarter of unfolded model.

Our goal of calculating the size of the base is to compute the length of FG. We notice that GH, half of FG looks to be the same size as BH, though we will need to prove it.

We will do the calculation by the following steps:

(1) Compute length of BH. We do this by computing the length of BC and HC and then subtracting.
(2) Show GH is the same length as BH.
(3) With the length of GH calculated, double the length of GH to get FG.

In all these calculations, we use expressions and not actual numbers. This makes things EASIER if and when you accept the use of symbols!

The size of BC, the diagonal of a square, makes use of one of the facts mentioned above, namely #1. The length is the side of *this* square, the quarter square, times the square root of 2.

$$BC = \text{side} \times \sqrt{2} \quad (\text{side represents the length of the side of the quarter square})$$

Recall that we made a preliminary fold of CD over to lie on CB. The length of CH is equal to the length of CD. This means that we can make an expression for HB. It is the length of the diagonal minus the length of the side.

$$HB = CB - CH$$

This is the same as

$$HB = \text{side} \times \sqrt{2} - \text{side}$$

But now we need to recall that side here is actually one-half the side of the original square. Let's call the length of the original square S. Then side in the last equation is half of S, which we write S × 0.5. Therefore

$$HB = (S \times 0.5) \times \sqrt{2} - (S \times 0.5)$$

Our goal is not HB, but HG. Actually, our goal is FG, but if we could determine HG, then we can double it to get FG. We are close. We need to focus now on angles.

The triangles CHG and CDG are congruent based on their origami construction. Also, triangles CHG and CDG are symmetry around CG. The edge CD is placed to line up with CB (as we have said before).

Angle HCD is 45 degrees.

Angle CHG is 90 degrees, from the two triangles being congruent and so is equal to CDB.

Therefore, angle BHG is (180 − CHG) = 90 degrees.

Angle CBG is half of 90 degrees: it was constructed by making a diagonal fold.

This means that two of the angles of the triangle BHG are 90 and 45 degrees, so the third angle must be 45 degrees. (This was explained in Fact #2.) This means that the triangle has two equal sides, namely HB and HG. So, HG is equal to the expression we determined for HB.

$$HG = HB = (S \times 0.5) \times \sqrt{2} - (S \times 0.5)$$

Doubling it, we have determined that the side of the base of the Star Basket is

$$\text{side of base} = 2 \times ((S \times 0.5) \times \sqrt{2} - (S \times 0.5))$$

We can simplify the expression: multiplying by 2 gets rid of those pesky .5 factors

$$\text{side of base} = S \times \sqrt{2} - S$$

Now some would say that this calculation is unnecessary because someone could measure the base. This is true, but that approach means you have to measure the base each time, for each new size paper. It also does not help if you knew what size base you wanted and wanted to determine what size paper would produce that size base. Our motivation for including this calculation is that the construction uses origami and mathematics. For example, the fact that the two triangles CHG and CDG are congruent is because of the folding. Our fingers do most of the mathematics!

Enhancements and Next Steps

When using standard kami, with white on one side and another color or design on the other, you need to think what is showing where on the final model. The Star Basket is a case in which both sides are visible. In the final model we show here (Figures 2.2 and 2.35), we made the inside of the basket and the flaps be white. Switching also could produce a nice effect.

The four triangular points of the Star Basket provide a place to make drawings and/or make folds. You can do the same thing to all four points or do something different, perhaps a face on one point and something like arms or legs on two points, and then a body.

More boxes and containers are coming as well as more action models. The next chapter is on what may be the oldest origami model: the Waterbomb. We also include a Tulip, a model with a folding sequence similar to that of the waterbomb. You also will learn how to make a Stem. Lastly, the next chapter will include the Stellated Octahedron. In the chapter, we will examine similarities and differences in the folding for these three models.

Exercises and Explorations

1. Practice making the square base (aka the preliminary base) and the waterbomb base, including unfolding (we could say "uncollapsed") and popping or pushing the center to unclasped the other way. You will see that both bases have four flaps. For each base, what are the mountain folds? That is, did they come from the original book folds or the diagonal folds or both?

2. Continuing the comparison of the square base and the waterbomb base, make two models, one square base, and one waterbomb base, from two sheets of the same size paper and compare. When folded flat, the waterbomb base is an isosceles right triangle. The square base is a square and also a diamond. Compare a folded edge of one with the folded edge of the other by lining up one with the other. Which is bigger? Is this supported by your answer to Exercise 1?

3. Research the origins of the degree system for measuring angles. Do some research on *radian* that is another unit for measuring angles.

4. The Star Basket is an opportunity to use pretty paper. Do pay attention to what is on the inside and the outside and, also, what is on the four triangles. The four triangles of the Star Basket provide a place to make drawings. You also can make variations by making folds on the point. Enhance your model.

5. Close the book. Be prepared to unfold and refold your model and sketch origami diagrams of the Fluttering Butterfly. You will need to make a comment about the fold over your finger. You can call this a "to taste" fold.

6. Make diagrams for the Business Card Frog. Again, you will need to indicate the "to taste" folds.

7. How would you describe—without a photo or a video—the action step that makes the Butterfly flutter?

8. Close the book. Be prepared to unfold and refold your model and sketch origami diagrams of the Star Basket.

9. Make diagrams for the Magazine Cover Box.

10. Review and compare the symmetries in the Fluttering Butterfly and in the Star Basket.

Chapter 3

Waterbomb, Tulip, and Stellated Octahedron

Background

The models for this chapter are the Waterbomb, the Tulip with Stem, also a traditional model, and Sam Ciulla's Stellated Octahedron.

The Waterbomb, shown in Figure 3.1, is one of the oldest known origami models.

Figure 3.1. Waterbomb.

Though Jeanine was not a young child at the time, she does remember filling the waterbomb with water and dropping it in a stairwell. You are encouraged to try it.

The Tulip is similar to the Waterbomb. It is shown here in Figure 3.2, with a stem made from a separate piece of paper. Making the stem gives us a chance to show the *kite base*.

Figure 3.2.   Tulip with stem.

The Stellated Octahedron designed by Sam Ciulla, shown in Figure 3.3, appears to be a much more complex shape than either of the first two, but has similarities to the other models. You can do it! We also will show how it is an octahedron with a pyramid coming out of each of the eight faces. These points are why the model is termed *stellated*, "like a star". The model also is described as the augmented octahedron.

Figure 3.3. Stellated Octahedron.

In the Explanations section, we will describe a way of describing the folding steps for these three models, which can aid your understanding of any model. You can learn how to calculate the final dimensions of the Waterbomb and given an exercise about the surface area.

SUPPLIES

Waterbomb
   Square paper: for the first time, we suggest 10-inch kami, and have smaller paper available for a second model. Some people like to fold small things!
Tulip and Stem
   A square of a color appropriate for a flower AND a second square, same size, green. Again, it is good to have supplies for a second model.
Stellated Octahedron
   A 10-inch square, at least for the first attempt.

Instructions

Waterbomb

The Waterbomb is one of the oldest origami models. Start with a square sheet of paper, such as the origami paper called kami, one side white and the other another color or a design, white side up as shown in Figure 3.4.

Figure 3.4.   Start with a square.

Orient the paper to be a diamond shape. Figure 3.5 shows an arrow indicating the direction and a dashed line telling you to make a valley fold matching the top point with the opposite point. We have chosen to use arrows in some of the diagrams for this model. Note: arrows also may be used in diagrams to rotate the paper, keeping it flat on the surface OR picking up the paper and turning it over. Generally, these arrows are thicker and there may be (should be) a guide.

If it is easier for you to fold away from yourself or towards yourself or left or right to control the paper better, please do so. Make the point's line up accurately and also check that the crease lines on the two other points come to a point. This step bisects the angles at the sides.

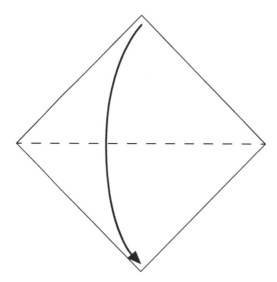

Figure 3.5.   Fold point to opposite point.

The result is shown in Figure 3.6. A triangle is formed.

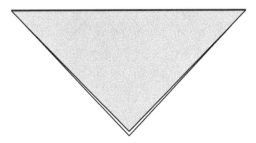

Figure 3.6. Paper folded to a triangle.

Now unfold the paper. Figure 3.7 shows the diamond again, but now with a crease marked.

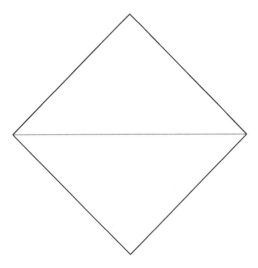

Figure 3.7. Unfolded paper, showing crease.

Now rotate the paper to the orientation shown in Figure 3.8.

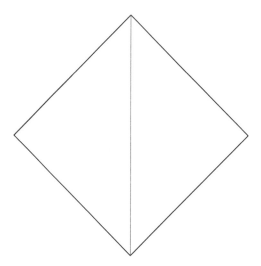

Figure 3.8.   Paper with crease, now vertical.

Now make another point to point, that is, diagonal fold. Figure 3.9 shows the crease from the previous step, a dashed line indicating a valley fold, and an arrow.

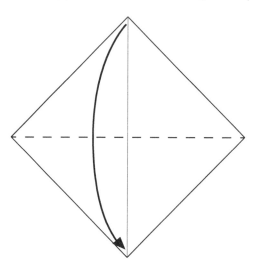

Figure 3.9.   Make second diagonal fold.

The result is shown in Figure 3.10. It is a triangle, with a crease marked.

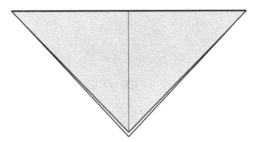

Figure 3.10.   Result of second diagonal fold.

Unfold. Figure 3.11 shows a diamond shape, with two crease lines.

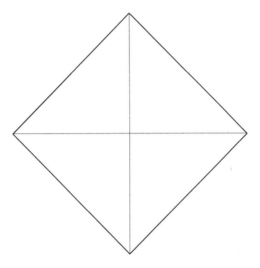

Figure 3.11.   Unfolded paper, showing two creases.

Now turn the paper over and orient to be a square. Figure 3.12 shows the paper, now on the color side, oriented as a square and indicating by dash-dot lines that the previous creases are mountain creases.

Figure 3.12.   Diagram showing sense of previous folds.

We are including the last diagram to show the results of turning the model over and oriented to be a square. Figure 3.13 indicates the next step is to make a book fold: top edge to bottom edge, making a crease through the X, the diagonals made in the previous steps. Again: experiment and determine what direction works best for you: towards you, away from you, going left or going right.

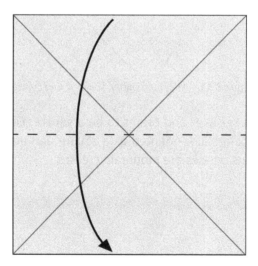

Figure 3.13.   Make book fold.

The results are shown in Figure 3.14. Notice that the white side is showing. (By the way, the caption hints at what will follow—there will be a second book fold.)

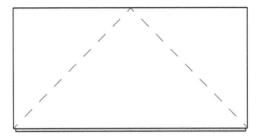

Figure 3.14. Result of first book fold.

Unfold. Figure 3.15 indicates the two diagonal folds that are mountain folds on this side (the color side) of the paper, and the book fold just made, which is a valley fold on this side of the paper. Note that we are showing the sense (valley fold versus mountain fold) of all the creases instead of using thin lines for folds already made.

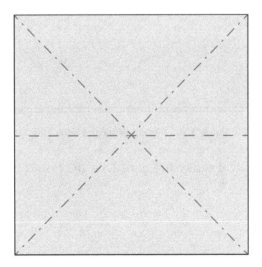

Figure 3.15. Unfolded paper, indicating folds.

Make a quarter turn and make another book fold, as indicated in Figure 3.16.

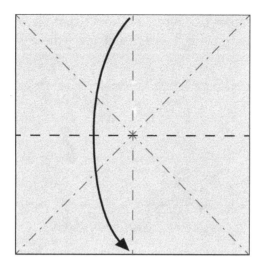

Figure 3.16.   Instruction to make second book fold.

Figure 3.17 shows result of second book fold.

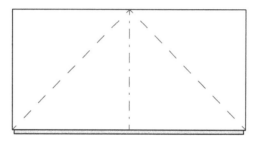

Figure 3.17.   Result of second book fold.

Unfold to see what is shown in Figure 3.18, the results of all the folds so far.

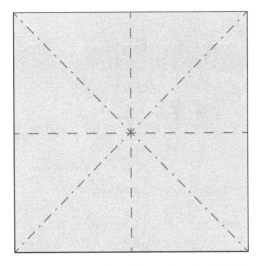

Figure 3.18. Results of diagonal and book folds.

This should look familiar to you—sort of. Recall the Business Card Frog. The paper probably is not lying flat but resembles what is shown in Figure 3.19.

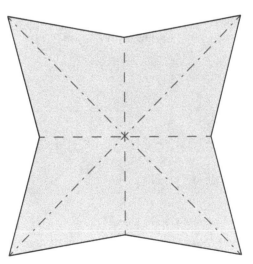

Figure 3.19. Paper may resemble tent.

Push in the sides to collapse the paper into a triangle. See Figure 3.20.

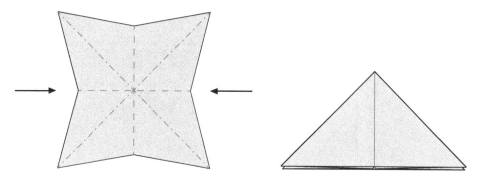

Figure 3.20.   Collapsed waterbomb base.

This is called the *waterbomb base*. Sometimes, but less frequently, it is called the *triangle* or *triangular base* to contrast with the square base (aka the preliminary base). We feel the need to tell you all the names because you may encounter them in books or directions online. Both bases use the same folds: book folds (edge to opposite edge) on one side of the paper and diagonal folds (point to opposite point) on the other. The *square base* (*preliminary base*) is constructed by pushing in the creases made by the diagonal folds. The waterbomb base is constructed by pushing in the creases made by the book folds (edge to edge). Practice doing this and you will understand (Figure 3.21).

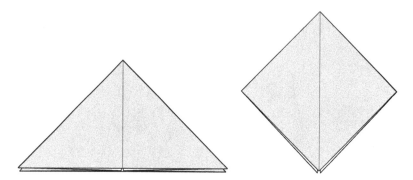

Figure 3.21.   Waterbomb base (left) and square base (right).

Now let's keep going to make the Waterbomb!

For future models, such as the Tulip, we do not need to start from Figure 3.4, but just say: make a waterbomb base. The same applies to any of the bases. Now sometimes the waterbomb base is showing the color and sometimes not, so you need to be careful about that (or possibly end up with an understated white model).

The next steps (we are combining two steps) is to fold one layer (one flap) at each corner, pivoting at the center, so that the folded edge aligns with the crease from the top point to the bottom edge. The valley fold indicated by the dashed line bisects the right angle. Do this on both sides. (Keep the model symmetric.) We don't know how standard this is but many of us call this an Oh-oh fold. Imagine putting both hands on your face. See Figure 3.22.

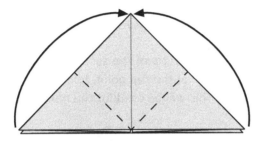

Figure 3.22. Oh-oh folds.

The diagram shown in Figure 3.23 uses heavy lines to indicate folded edges and cut edges lying at the top of the paper. There are layers. There are four flaps.

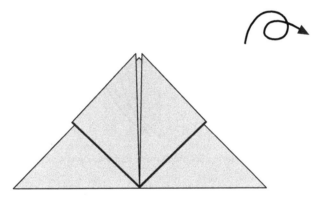

Figure 3.23. Complete two Oh-oh folds.

Now turn the model over. Figure 3.24 indicates a smooth side, with a vertical crease indicating a previous fold and two dashed lines indicating another pair of Oh-oh folds.

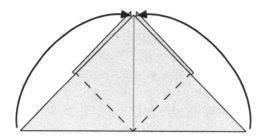

Figure 3.24.   Model turned over and next oh-oh folds.

Figure 3.25 indicates the results of the second pair of Oh-oh folds, and the instructions for the next step: at the top point, fold one layer to the bottom and make a small pinch mark. This will be used for the next step.

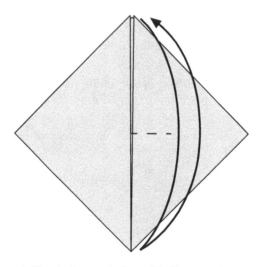

Figure 3.25.   Indicates pinch mark half way on the vertical.

The next pair of steps is to fold the side points to the middle. The pinch mark is used to indicate the middle. You only have to make one mark, because it is easy to make the other side match. (Note: some of us don't even make a mark but judge the center by bringing the point on the side to the center line and checking that the folded edge is parallel to the center line.) See Figure 3.26.

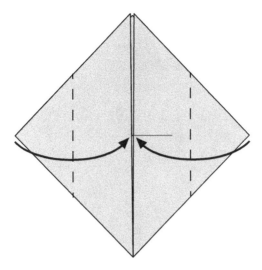

Figure 3.26. Fold sides to center.

Figure 3.27 shows the result.

Figure 3.27. Sides folded to center.

Turn over the model. You will see in Figure 3.28 the pinch mark again, but you may not need it since you can line up the folding with the folds on what is not underneath.

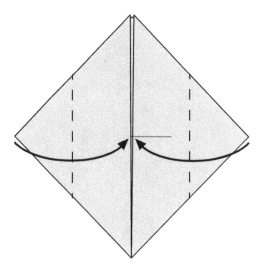

Figure 3.28.   Directions to repeat folding in of sides.

Figure 3.29 shows the results. The Oh-oh folds and the folding in the sides, each involving four steps. The model will exhibit symmetries: bilateral symmetry (side to side) in the front and the back.

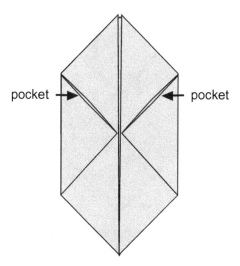

Figure 3.29.   Model in lozenge shape.

The next set of folds is repeated for each flap: twice in the front and then turn the model over and repeat two more times. At the top, you will notice that there are loose flaps: two in the front and two behind. The objective is to tuck these flaps into pockets (slots). The valley fold line in Figure 3.30 indicates the location of the pocket. However, the tucking operation is made up of three steps. The first is to fold the loose flap to the right along the line indicated.

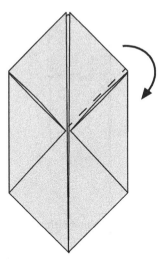

Figure 3.30. Instruction for first step of tucking operation.

Figure 3.31 shows the result of this first step. The next step is indicated by another valley fold: fold the triangle flap in half.

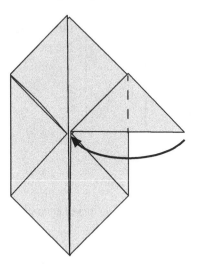

Figure 3.31. Result of folding flap out to the right.

These steps make what we can call a tab, which now ready to be tucked into the pocket. See Figure 3.32.

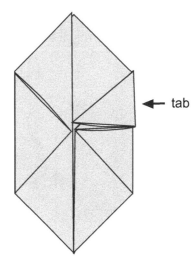

Figure 3.32.   Flap prepared for tucking into pocket.

Figure 3.33 indicates that the tab is tucked into the pocket.

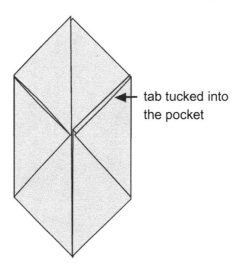

Figure 3.33.   Flap tucked into pocket.

Repeat this sequence of three folds three more times: once on the left side, then turn the model over and repeat two times more. These four tucking-in-the-flap operations are the locks that hold the model together.

Figure 3.34 indicates two more folds. These are preparation folds, meaning that you make the fold and then unfold it. The top point is folded down to the center and the bottom point folded up to the center. Unfold both of these folds.

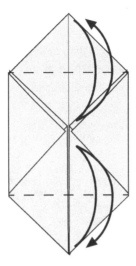

Figure 3.34. Instructions for preparation folds.

Turn the model over and repeat. This prepared the paper for the last step.

Pick up the model. You will notice that the bottom end has a small hole and the top one does not. Hold the model by separating the flaps. Blow into the hole with a short, strong breath. Figure 3.35 shows Jeanine's daughter, Aviva, blowing into the model. This will inflate the model to be three dimensional (3D). You can decide if you want to flatten the top and bottom faces to be a cube, that is, a six-sided shape or reinforce the top and the bottom four triangular sides meeting at a point.

Figure 3.35. Aviva blowing into the waterbomb.

Tulip Flower

As is the practice in directions, the instructions for this model can be abbreviated by simply stating to start with a waterbomb base, followed by Oh-oh folds, front and back. (If you need to, look above at the instructions) See Figure 3.36 for where the Tulip instructions begin. We will use photos, because there are situations when making this model in which we want to show folds in process, including showing hands.

Figure 3.36.   Waterbomb base, followed by Oh-oh folds, front and back.

You should have two flaps on each side. Turn a flap on the left over to the right. You will now see a smooth side. See Figures 3.37 and 3.38. Recall: this is called a *minor miracle*.

Figure 3.37. Turning left flap over to the right.

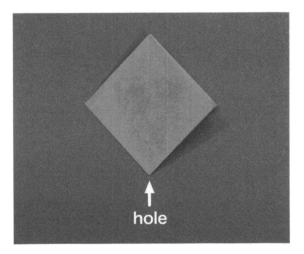

Figure 3.38. Smooth side facing up.

Turn the model over and repeat. You now should have a smooth side here also. See Figures 3.39 and 3.40.

Figure 3.39.   Another turning left flap over to the right.

Figure 3.40.   Another smooth side facing up.

Make sure the little hole is at the bottom and the top has four flaps, each with multiple layers.

You now are going to make locks as you did before, but this time one lock in front and one lock in the back. Do this by folding each of the two sides—starting from the end opposite the hole—a little *past* the center line. See Figure 3.41.

Figure 3.41. Fold starting from the top and a little pasting the center line.

Now tuck one side into the other. Figure 3.42 shows this in process, and Figure 3.43 shows the tuck in complete on one side of the model.

Figure 3.42. Tucking one side into the other.

Figure 3.43.   Done the tuck on one side.

Turn the model over and repeat. You can use the first side to gauge where to fold the flaps. See Figures 3.44 and 3.45.

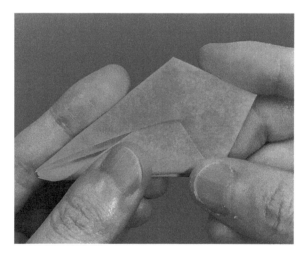

Figure 3.44.   Tucking one side into the other on the other side.

Figure 3.45. Done the tuck on both sides.

Since we want the base to be curved and not a crisp edge, we won't direct you to do a preparation fold at the base as was suggested for the regular Waterbomb.

Hold the model as shown in Figure 3.46 and blow into the hole to inflate as was done for the Waterbomb.

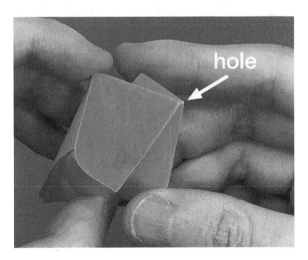

Figure 3.46. Holding the model and indicating the hole to blow into.

The Tulip does need some post-3D shaping. Make the petals petal-like, by taking a pen or pencil and curling them. Finally, the tulip is done (Figures 3.47 and 3.48).

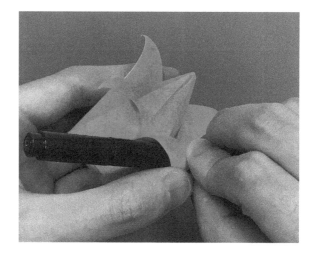

Figure 3.47.   Curling the petals with a pen.

Figure 3.48.   Tulip is completed.

Stem and Leaf

The hole in the base of the tulip flower can be used for a stem, or more accurately, a stem–leaf combination. Take a new square sheet of paper, preferably a green color. The stem is made starting with white side up, a diagonal fold (Figure 3.49).

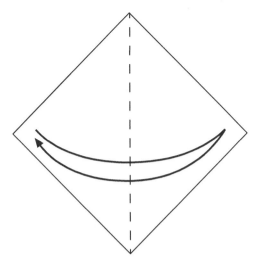

Figure 3.49. First diagonal fold.

Unfold and then fold sides to the crease just made (Figure 3.50).

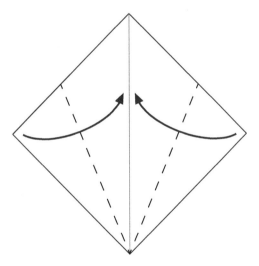

Figure 3.50. Fold sides to the center crease line.

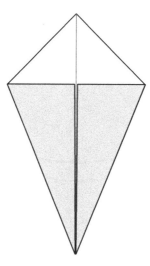

Figure 3.51.   Kite Base.

The results are shown in Figure 3.51. This is called the *Kite base*, though we must admit that some of us call this the *Ice Cream Cone*. Rotate the model. Now fold the raw edges on the bottom to the center.

This is called the *Diamond base*. See Figures 3.52 and 3.53.

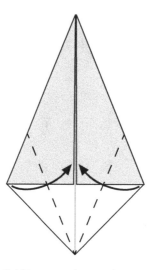

Figure 3.52.   Fold bottom edges to the center crease line.

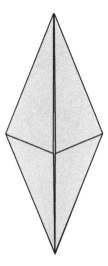

Figure 3.53. Diamond Base.

Now skinny the bottom by folding the edges in to the center again (See Figure 3.54). Figure 3.55 shows the results.

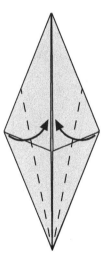

Figure 3.54. Skinny the bottom.

Figure 3.55.   Result of the previous folds.

Turn model over. This will be the smooth side. Fold the model in half by folding bottom point to meet the top point. See Figures 3.56 and 3.57.

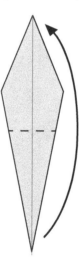

Figure 3.56.   Fold the model in half.

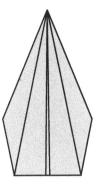

Figure 3.57. Result of the previous fold.

The instruction now is to fold the whole model in half by folding the left side over the right side. See Figures 3.58 and 3.59.

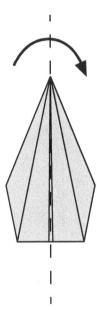

Figure 3.58. Folding the left side over the right side.

Figure 3.59.   Result of the previous fold.

Now carefully pull down the leftmost layer. This will be the leaf. You can curl this, also. See Figure 3.60.

Figure 3.60.   Curling the leaf with finger.

Put the stem into the hole at the bottom of the tulip. See Figure 3.61.

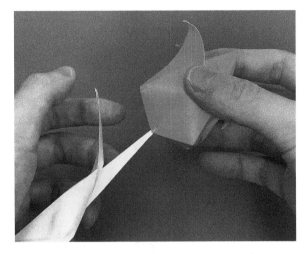

Figure 3.61.   Inserting a stem into the tulip.

Stellated Octahedron

The name of this model, Sam Ciulla's Stellated Octahedron, describes the shape: a point comes out of each of eight faces, giving the model a star-like quality. You can examine this when you are done.

Because this is the third of three models for this chapter, the directions here are complete, but somewhat accelerated. This is intended to encourage you to reflect on what you are doing, which will help you remember how to make the model. You will be doing a lot of folding, but because of the symmetries (bilaterally in two dimensions), it should seem like less than it is.

RESOURCES

You can find directions for Sam Ciulla's Stellated Octahedron online (Jeremy Shafer has an excellent video) and in books. (See **The Art of Origami** by Gay Merrill Gross.)

We start with a challenge. The first phase of the folding is to produce a grid of 4 × 4 squares, with an X in each one as shown in Figure 3.62.

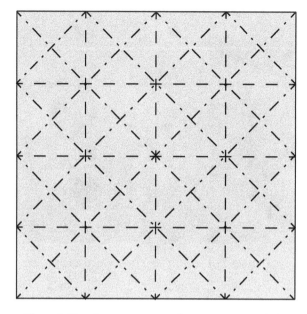

Figure 3.62. Crease patterns of 4 × 4 squares and X's.

Note: The creases parallel to the edges are valley folds on the color side. The X creases are mountain folds on the color side. When we make them, we will be making valley folds on the white side. Before reading on, try to think how to produce the grid with X's.

Let's start with the 4 × 4 grid. You know how to do this: make book folds, unfold and then cupboard folds. Unfold, rotate the paper, and repeat. Figure 3.63 shows the result of these steps.

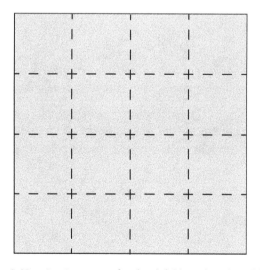

Figure 3.63. 4 × 4 squares after book folds and cupboard folds.

Now let's focus on the X's. The critical idea is to NOT think of these as individual X's! You can say that our challenge was a case of mis-direction. Instead, think about diagonal folds. Look at the figure and observe the results of one fold made point to point and then, paper rotated, the other fold made point to opposite point. Then add several more folds parallel to these folds. You will read how to accomplish this and the Explanations section has more detail on what the folds do.

Turn the paper over to the white side and orient it to be a diamond. Make the two diagonal folds as indicated in Figure 3.64.

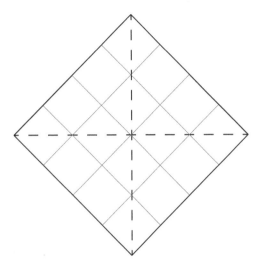

Figure 3.64.   Two diagonal folds.

Figure 3.65 shows the next four folds. These are produced by folding each corner to the center. This has the name in origami circles of *blintz fold*. (Of course, it is not how to make an edible blintz, which is a rolled filled pastry, and surely Lillian Oppenheimer knew this, but that is the adopted term.)

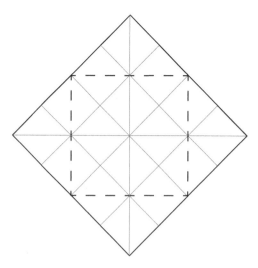

Figure 3.65.   Four folds by folding each corner to the center. Valley folds for blintz fold.

Unfold. The next set of folds is to fold each corner to the crease line made by the blintz folding on the *other* side of the main diagonal. The diagram shows the target line with an X. See Figure 3.66.

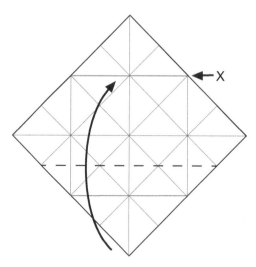

Figure 3.66.   Indicating a line with X to which we fold the bottom corner.

Unfold. Rotate the model a quarter turn and repeat three more times, unfolding each time. See Figure 3.67.

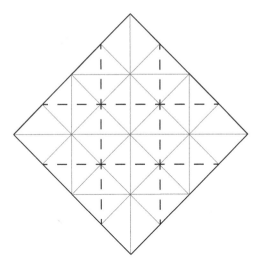

Figure 3.67. Four valley folds after folding each corner to the crease line made by the blintz fold.

Now fold each corner to the nearest crease line. These are the same crease lines made by the blintz folding. Keep these folds in place. See Figures 3.68 and 3.69.

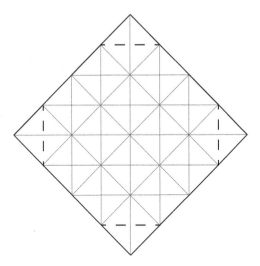

Figure 3.68. Fold each corner to the nearest crease line.

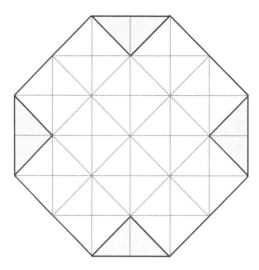

Figure 3.69.   Keeping the last folds in place.

Collapse the model as you have collapsed to form a waterbomb base. Here is a photo of the collapse in process (Figure 3.70). Figure 3.71 shows the collapse complete.

Figure 3.70.   Collapsing in process.

Figure 3.71. Collapse is completed.

Stop for a moment and observe that this is pretty close to a waterbomb base with some extra folding.

The next step is to make locks. For the Stellated Octahedron model, there will be two locks on the front side and then the model is turned over and the locking step repeated. The model has lost some of the symmetry: it is still symmetric left to right, but not top to bottom.

To make the first lock, we have the familiar situation with two flaps on each side. Fold over one flap on the right side to the point indicated on the left (Figure 3.72).

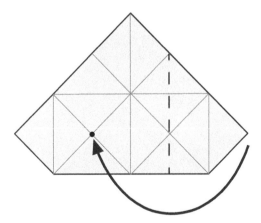

Figure 3.72. Bring the right side to the point indicated.

Figure 3.73 shows the result and the next step, which is to fold the point back to the right.

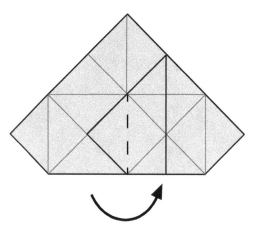

Figure 3.73.   Fold the point back to the right figure.

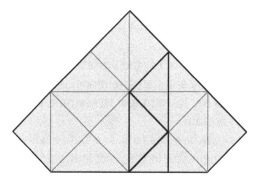

Figure 3.74.   Result of the previous fold.

You have constructed a pocket. Put the bottom triangle into the pocket. (Figures 3.74 and 3.75) Figure 3.76 shows the process.

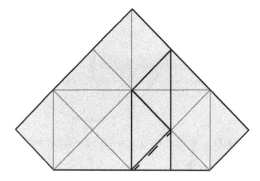

Figure 3.75.   Put the bottom triangle into the pocket.

Figure 3.76.   Inserting the triangle in the pocket.

Now repeat this on the left side and then turn the model over and repeat it two more times. You now have a hexagon shape as shown in Figure 3.77.

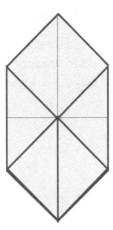

Figure 3.77.   Hexagon shapes after repeating the procedure three more times.

There will be a hole at the bottom, so repeat what you did for the previous models to inflate the model: make the model three dimensional by giving a short, strong blow into the hole. You may need to do some shaping to achieve the stellated shape. See Figure 3.78 for the resulting model.

Figure 3.78. Model after blowing into the hold at the bottom.

Explanations

Producing the X's in the Stellated Octahedron

We first want to explain why the procedure described for the Stellated Octahedron produces the X's. The requirement is to produce the main diagonal folds and then make creases parallel to the two diagonals. Figure 3.79 indicates the distances.

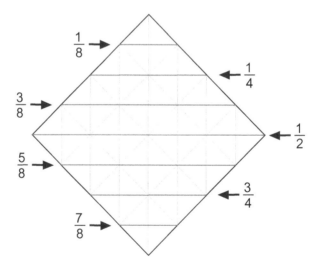

Figure 3.79. Distance indicating from the top.

The corner-to-corner folds produce the crease lines at the 1/2 mark. The blintz folding produces the 1/4 and 3/4 crease lines. Why? Because we are folding the corner to the halfway point. This halves each half! Now producing the 1/8 may be clear: we folded a corner to the 1/4 mark, the crease produced by the blintz folding. Doing this made the 1/8 mark by halving 1/4. Producing the 7/8 crease line required rotating the paper and folding the corner to the next crease line, which, again, was produced by the blintz folding. We are making progress with only two more crease lines to discuss. Recall from the instructions that we folded a corner to the line made by the blintz on the other side of the main diagonal. This line is 1/4 from the corner. See Figure 3.80.

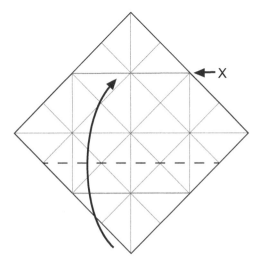

Figure 3.80.   Making 5/8 by folding the corner to the 1/4 line.

This fold has the effect of halving the three-quarter distance. Half of three-quarters is three-eighths. The instructions directed you to do that for all four corners, so this produced the crease lines at 3/8 from each end. The 3/8 from one end is the same as 5/8 from the other end. See Figure 3.81.

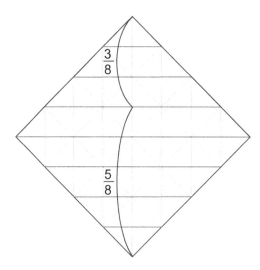

Figure 3.81.   The 3/8 from one end is the same as 5/8 from the other end.

Comparing Models

It is obvious that these models have similarities. One way to describe the similarities and differences is to group steps into stages that accomplish similar things. This is what we are doing when we say: make a waterbomb base. Combining several steps and calling it one step is a common practice in many disciplines. In computer programming, operations are combined to make new entities, called by various names: macros, functions, procedures, subroutines, methods; each with its distinct meaning, but all indicating ways of building on and extending the original language. In mathematics, there are functions. In origami, mathematics, and computer programming, time is spent comparing the combinations of steps.

Origami has its own *jargon* for combinations of steps. For example, you made squash folds. Most notably, you have read about origami bases. You may be accustomed to thinking of jargon in a negative sense, but in any field, jargon serves an important function. Grouping steps in origami, using established origami names or your own terminology, and grouping the groups together, helps us focus on how and why the paper is manipulated in space.

TIP FOR TEACHERS

People like to know a model "by heart." In our class presentations, students were urged to sum up the folding in their own words and origami and mathematics jargon. Grouping steps, including pointing out symmetries, not only encourages mathematical thinking but helps in remembering how to make a model.

Thinking about these models, we organize the folding sequence into four stages. The grouping/sequencing works for these models and the exercises include challenges for you to apply this structure to other models.

1. Initial construction
2. Making the locks
3. 2D to 3D
4. Shaping in 3D

With this big picture, let's go into detail. The Initial construction for the Waterbomb and the Tulip starts with the waterbomb base. The Stellated Octahedron is different, but only somewhat different. The initial construction stage includes preparation folds. See the exercises for a challenge about the Stellated Octahedron.

You recall there was a lock with the very first model, the Magazine Cover Box. The models in this chapter also each have locks. Look again at Figures 3.33, 3.42 and 3.76, to observe the similarities and differences. The locks hold the model together when it becomes—is changed—to be three dimensional.

The change from 2D to 3D is the same operation. Hopefully, you now have mastered blowing into the hole with a strong, short breath.

The shaping after the model is 3D varies among the models. The plain water-bomb may need reinforcing of the edges. The Tulip needs curling the petals to be flower-like. The Stem also required shaping.

Consider doing this type of analysis for other models.

Examining the Waterbomb

The final shape of the waterbomb is a cube. Here is an exercise to explore the cube. Take a finished Waterbomb, color the outside. Before unfolding, try to envision what you will see. Will the marking all be on one side? Will it be connected? Will there be holes? We include a photo, but please try to do the exercise. It is fun!

Unfold. What do you see? Was it what you expected?

Figure 3.82. Unfolded waterbomb with colored faces that used to be the outside.

You can re-fold the model and see the cube emerging from the flat paper and we recommend that you do this. See Figure 3.82.

What can we deduce from this exercise? There are three squares plus pieces that make up three more. In particular, there are three squares in the middle of the paper, with half a square at each side. You can convince yourself, possibly by folding the center square to lie on top of each one next to it and by folding the half-squares on top of one of the whole squares, that these squares all have the same size. Since there are 3 + one-half + one-half, the length is one-quarter of the size of the side of the original square piece of paper.

Now let us show you a different way to calculate the length of the side of the middle square. Let's go back in the folding procedure to the making of the Oh-oh folds. See Figures 3.22 and 3.23. We have taken the second figure and added labels and a bold line in Figure 3.83. What is the length of the bold line representing DE, the base of the triangle ADE?

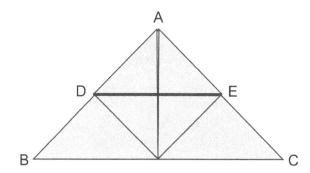

Figure 3.83. Comparing triangle ADE and triangle ABC.

The triangle ADE is similar to the triangle ABC because the angles are the same from the following reasoning. One angle, BAC and DAE, is the same angle. It is a 90-degree angle. The sides AE and AD are equal because of the folding. This means that the two angles ADE and AED facing these sides are the same and that means they are each 45 degrees. So the big triangle, ABC, is similar to the little triangle, ADE. Now AE is half of AC because of the folding: the edge AC is halved. Then, because of the properties of similar triangles, the length DE—the bold line—is half the length BC.

We are half-way there. Recalling the next steps in the folding, look back at Figure 3.27. We have taken that diagram and added labels and another bold line. See Figure 3.84. The labels A, D, and E represent what they did before, and we have added two circles on the bold line.

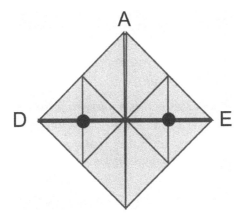

Figure 3.84. Continuing calculation.

The distance between the two circles is half the length of the line DE. This is because folding each corner in halves that part of the line. The folding halves half. Since the length of DE was half the original side of the square, this means the edge between the circles is one-quarter of the side of the original square. This is what our observations from coloring the cube and unfolding the paper told us.

Stellated Octahedron Stellation

The Stellated Octahedron appears to be a polyhedron with many more than eight faces. However, another way to look at it is to view it as having eight faces with each face changed into a pyramid. You can see this if you color each pyramid a different color. You will see eight colors. See the photo in Figure 3.85 showing four pyramids seen from one side.

Figure 3.85.   The face of each pyramid is a distinct color.

Enhancements and Next Steps

This is not an enhancement as much as a party trick. The Stellated Octahedron is an action model! If you place it so that the hole points up, and you should do this casually so your audience does not notice that you are doing anything special in the placement, yell "MOVE" or something else and the model will roll over. If someone else tries to do this, there is a good chance that they will not position the hole pointing up and it won't work. The explanation for this is that the model has the locks around the hole and this makes it top-heavy when you place it with the hole facing up.

In Chapter 5, you will learn how to make the *Waterbomb Base Ornament*. The waterbomb base is the unit and six units can be combined to make the ornament. This is what is called a modular model and there are more modulars in **More Origami with Explanations**.

In the following chapter, you will learn a practical model: the *Drinking Cup*.

Exercises and Explorations

1. What was the result of the exercise of coloring the outside of the model? Was it what you thought? Compute the total surface area, that is, do a calculation in 2D computing and adding up the sizes of the colored areas.
2. Calculate final dimensions of tulip base and its height.

3. Calculate the final dimensions of the stem. You will need to define the "to taste" fold or calculate a range for the height.

4. Consider the Stellated Octahedron and describe the folding in terms of the four stages.

5. Compare the location of the extra folds in the Stellated Octahedron and the regular Waterbomb. Why don't they perform the same way?

6. Color the Stellated Octahedron, make a prediction, and then take the model apart. If you have eight markers of different colors, color each pyramid by making dots and color the surrounding area a solid color. Take the model apart and see what you have produced.

7. You just learned the origami term *blintz fold*, but you probably know this fold from making a model called the Fortune Teller or, in Jeanine's family, the Nose Grabber. Produce diagrams and instructions using origami and math language for this model.

Chapter 4

Drinking Cup

Background

The model for this chapter is a practical Drinking Cup that is made from a square, but can be made from ordinary copier paper (8.5 × 11). The model starts with what many would describe as an unusual fold, which will be discussed in the Explanations section.

    The Drinking Cup may have been invented independent of origami (Figure 4.1). If anyone has information on its origins, please let us know.

Figure 4.1. Drinking Cup.

Instructions

Drinking Cup

Let's make the assumption that you need a Drinking Cup and do not have square origami paper available. Start with ordinary copier paper (8.5 × 11) and fold the short side to the long side. See Figure 4.2.

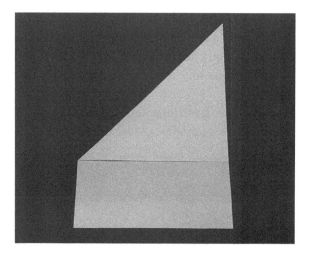

Figure 4.2.   Folding the short side to the long side to make a triangle.

Now fold the other short edge over the folded paper. See Figure 4.3.

Figure 4.3. Folding the other short edge over the folded paper.

Unfold and you can tear off the extra portion of paper, using the crease line as the line to cut (Figures 4.4 and 4.5) OR lift up the folded paper and tuck the paper under the folded piece (Figures 4.6 and 4.7).

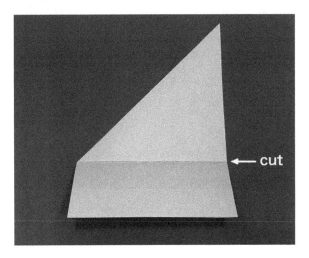

Figure 4.4. Line to cut is indicated.

Figure 4.5.   Cut off the extra portion of the paper.

Figure 4.6.   Tuck the extra portion under the folded paper.

Figure 4.7. Finishing up tucking.

At this point, we continue as if we had a square, with a diagonal fold. This is an isosceles triangle whose two sides have the same length. Orient the paper so that the folded edge is at the bottom. See Figure 4.8. The vertices (corners) of the triangle, which is made up of multiple layers of paper, are labeled A, B, and C.

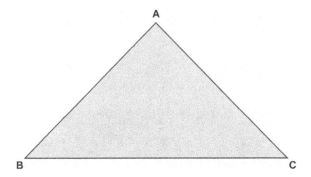

Figure 4.8. Triangle whose corners are labeled.

The next step is what we are describing as an unusual fold. So far in this book, most origami folds, involve taking an edge to an edge or a crease line or a corner vertex to an edge or a crease line. The operation here is to take vertex C and fold it to lie on edge AB defining new points D, E, and F such that the line DE is parallel to the line BC. This means that you need to carefully estimate the position of D. See Figures 4.9 and 4.10.

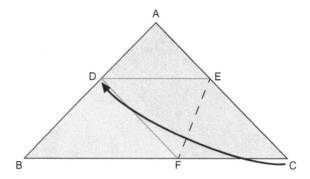

Figure 4.9.   Bring C to the estimated point D.

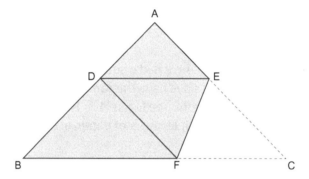

Figure 4.10.   DE parallel to BC.

Figure 4.11 shows the process, and Figure 4.12 shows the result.

Figure 4.11.   Process of estimating the position D.

Figure 4.12. Result of the previous fold.

This step is simpler than it sounds. However, the step merited discussion, which you will find in Explanations.

Turn the model over. Figure 4.13 shows the model turned over.

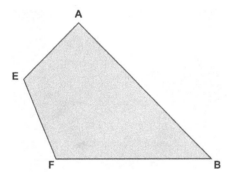

Figure 4.13. Model turned over.

Now repeat the last operation: fold the vertex B over to the opposite edge so that the resulting edge is parallel to the bottom bold. This step is easier than the first one because you can see the target of the fold. See Figure 4.14.

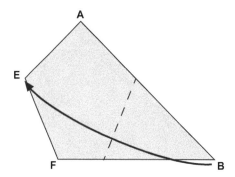

Figure 4.14.   Bring B to the estimated point E.

Figure 4.15 shows the process.

Figure 4.15.   Process of estimating the position E.

Figure 4.16. Result of the previous fold.

The last steps are to lock the model by folding the top points into the pockets. See Figure 4.16 it is easiest to do this in two steps for each point: fold one triangular layer *over* the folds made. See Figures 4.17 and 4.18.

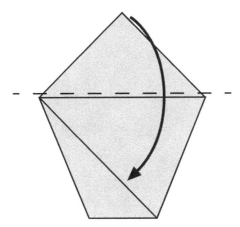

Figure 4.17. Fold one triangle over the folds just made.

Figure 4.18.   A triangle over the folds.

Now lift the triangular flap up and tuck it inside the pocket. See Figures 4.19 and 4.20.

Figure 4.19.   Tuck the triangle into the pocket.

Figure 4.20.   Done the tuck-in process.

Turn the model over. Repeat the two steps done on the other side: Fold the remaining layer down over the folds. See Figures 4.21 and 4.22.

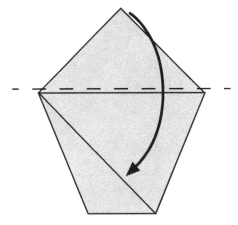

Figure 4.21.   Fold one triangle over the folds just made.

Figure 4.22.   A triangle over the folds.

Lift up and tuck the triangle into the pocket. See Figures 4.23 and 4.24.

Figure 4.23.   Tuck the triangle into the pocket.

Figure 4.24. Done the tuck-in process.

The Drinking Cup is nearly done. It is still 2D. Press the two ends to make it rounded. It is easy to shape it by sliding your finger in the pocket (Figure 4.25). Figure 4.26 shows the completed Drinking Cup.

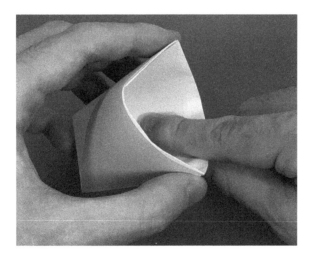

Figure 4.25. Shaping the cup.

Figure 4.26.   Completed Drinking Cup.

Explanations

Most folds in origami are specified by taking an edge to line up with another edge (for example, a book fold) or a crease line (cupboard fold) or taking an endpoint of an edge, perhaps a corner of the paper, to match an opposite point (diagonal fold). You also have seen instances of edges lined up with adjacent edges, resulting in bisecting an angle. The target edges, crease lines, or points are called landmarks. The directions for the model in this chapter indicate a fold by specifying that a point is to lie somewhere on one edge, such that the connecting edge is parallel to a third edge. This fold defines three points and we had to prove to ourselves that the positioning of the fold was *well-defined*, a mathematical term meaning there is one and only one way to do it. In fact, we needed to calculate the positioning of points in order to produce the diagrams.

Figure 4.27 shows the triangle ABC made by folding a square piece of paper, point to opposite point to make a triangle, and then showing the points D, E, and F made by folding the point marked C to meet the line AB and with the line formed DE parallel to BC.

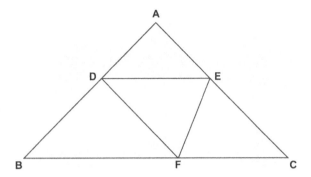

Figure 4.27.   Triangle with labels.

Triangle CEF is congruent to, exactly the same as, triangle DEF because one is placed on top of the other. This means that the length of the line segment D to E is equal to the line segment C to E. See Figure 4.28.

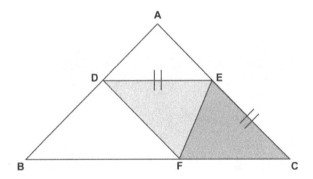

Figure 4.28.   Triangle CEF congruent to DEF and the distance DE equal to the distance CE.

Triangle ADE is similar to ABC based on the angles (see Figure 4.29). Remember: triangles are similar if the angles match.

- The angle at A is equal to itself.
- The angle formed by ADE is equal to angle ABC because of the line DE being parallel to BC and the line AB going through these two parallel lines.
- If two angles of triangles are the same, the third angle must be the same, so they are similar.

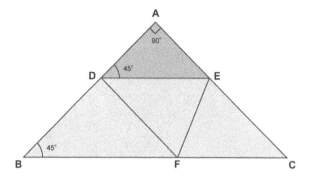

Figure 4.29. Triangle ADE similar to ABC.

Say the side of the original square is length S. Then the line BC is length times the square root of 2. (You have seen this before in the calculation of the length of the base of the Star Basket in Chapter 2.) We write this as $\sqrt{2}$S. See Figure 4.30.

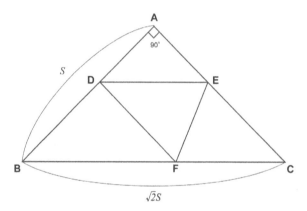

Figure 4.30. Triangle showing the lengths of AB and BC.

Our goal now is to compute the length of CE (which is equal to length of DE), so let's focus on the length of DE. (Note: at times, a line segment will be denoted by writing something like CE and at other times, CE will denote the length of the line segment. It should be clear from the context.)

The length of AE is equal to S − EC.

If two triangles are similar, then the ratios of the corresponding sides are all the same. (This was explained in the Background section in Chapter 2.) Therefore, the ratio of the bases of the two triangles, DE and BC, is equal to the ratio of the sides AE and AC.

$$\frac{DE}{BC} = \frac{AE}{AC}$$

Because AC is equal to S, we can substitute AC for S in the equation above. Also, DE = EC, BC = $\sqrt{2}$S, and AE = S − EC. Therefore, the equation can be rewritten as

$$\frac{EC}{\sqrt{2S}} = \frac{(S-EC)}{S}$$

Doing some algebraic manipulation, we solve for EC
Multiply both sides by $\sqrt{2}$S

$$\sqrt{2S} \times \frac{EC}{\sqrt{2S}} = \sqrt{2S} \times \frac{(S-EC)}{S}$$

$$EC = \sqrt{2}\left(S-EC\right)$$

$$\sqrt{2}EC + EC = \sqrt{2S}$$

$$\left(\sqrt{2}+1\right)EC = \sqrt{2S}$$

$$EC = \frac{\sqrt{2S}}{\sqrt{2}+1}$$

So, the length of EC is $\sqrt{2}S/(\sqrt{2}+1)$. This defines the point E exactly.

Continuing on to calculate FC. This is equal to FD. Now, we ask: is the triangle DBF similar to triangle ABC (and ADE)? It looks like it is, but looks aren't enough. Let's check the angles. When you are reading the text, use your finger to point to the relevant place in Figure 4.31.

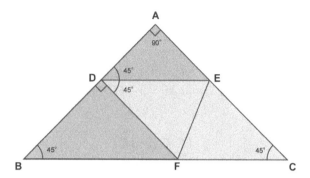

Figure 4.31.   Triangle indicating important angles.

The critical issue is the angle BDF. The angle ADE is 45 degrees because of the line AB intersecting two parallel lines. The angle EDF is 45 degrees because it corresponds to ECF. The two triangles fall on top of each other. So the angle BDF is 90 degrees because it and the two angles each 45 degrees must add up to 180 degrees. This means the DBF triangle is similar to triangle ABC and ADE. Then FD is equal to BD which is equal to CE, which was just calculated. Because FC = FD, FC is $\sqrt{2}S/(\sqrt{2}+1)$.

This all means that the fold intersections made by the operation of locating point C on the edge AB can be calculated in terms of the side of the original square!

Enhancements and Next Steps

The next chapter introduces modular origami, also called unit origami. The models are the Waterbomb Base Ornament (by Robert Neale) and the King David Crown designed by Laura Kruskal.

Exercises and Explorations

1. The Drinking Cup becomes three dimensional by pressing the sides. Describe the shapes that you can make the opening. You can make the opening be a circle. Calculate the length of the perimeter. Note: the perimeter stays the same length.
2. Paul Jackson has an action model, Kissing (or pecking) Birds that starts with the same folds as the Drinking Cup. Look it up and make it.
3. Describe the symmetries in the Drinking Cup.
4. The Drinking Cup may have a history independent of origami. Do some research and see if you can find the origins of this Drinking Cup and others.

Chapter 5

Waterbomb Base Ornament and King David Crown

Background

The models for this chapter belong to the category of origami called *modulars*, *modular origami* or *unit origami*. A *modular origami model* is made by combining a set number of units, each of the same or similar design. The Tulip with Stem shown in Chapter 3 would not be considered modular origami because the two pieces are very different and have identified roles in the combined product. In this chapter, we introduce you to origami by showing you two models.

The Waterbomb Base Ornament, designed by Robert Neale, shown in Figure 5.1, is made up of 6 waterbomb base units.

Figure 5.1. Waterbomb base ornament.

Laura Kruskal was known for her crowns and for many years designed a new one for each OrigamiUSA convention. Figure 5.2 shows Aviva and Annika each wearing Laura Kruskal's King David Crowns. Laura was a proponent of using ordinary, also termed *found paper*. Aviva's crown is made of recycled paper and Annika's from construction paper.

Figure 5.2.   Aviva and Annika wearing King David Crowns.

SUPPLIES

Modulars require multiple pieces of paper!

Waterbomb Base Ornament

This model requires six pieces of paper, and 6-inch kami is good for a start. Using three sets of two pieces of paper of the same color makes the construction easier.

Crown

The crown requires four pieces of construction paper (8.5 × 11) though ordinary copier paper would do. It can be four different colors or whatever you like. You can experiment with different sizes and types of paper. As you will see, the construction can be varied for different size heads.

Instructions

Waterbomb Base Ornament

For the Waterbomb Base Ornament, you know how to do the unit! Go back to Chapter 3 or look at the box below. Please make six waterbomb bases, three different colors (we mean color on one side and white on the other side. The color sides will be the outside and the white on the inside), with two of each color.

We are using red, white, and blue paper. The challenge in modular origami generally is in putting the pieces together. The individual unit often is easy to make. The ornament will have six units. This corresponds to the shape of a cube. A cube has six faces but it is better to think of them as three pairs of faces. In each pair, the two faces *face* each other. Think of how we might describe directions in space: up/down, left/right, forward/backward or up/down, east/west, north/south. We speak of space being three dimensional because it takes three values to specify a point.

Making this model, requiring six waterbomb bases, definitely will help you learn how to make waterbomb bases. Just in case you need a refresher, remember that the waterbomb base uses two book folds (edge to opposite edge) and two diagonal folds (corner (also called vertex) to the opposite corner). The book folds and the diagonal folds must be done on the opposite sides of the paper. For the waterbomb base, which in flattened form is a triangle, you make the diagonal folds starting on the white side, so the folded paper is a color triangle. Remember: color triangle leads to color-folded waterbomb base triangle. See Figure 5.3.

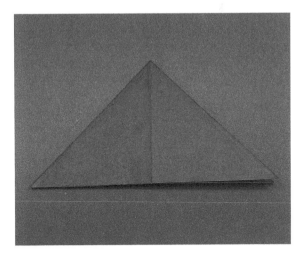

Figure 5.3. Waterbomb base.

Line up the six units. The units of the same color will face each other. Terms often used in constructing modular are *pockets and pokes* or *tabs and pockets*. A waterbomb base has four flaps. Hold it as shown in Figure 5.4. This model is built in three dimensions. That is, the units are not flat. Observe the four flaps.

Figure 5.4.   Waterbomb base with four flaps facing front.

The inside of the flaps are the *pockets* and the flap as a whole is a *poke*. Each piece will be connected to four other pieces. The fifth piece is the unit of the same color. Once you decide on the relationship of a piece of one color to a piece of a second color, it will not change. All the other connections will be the same. Furthermore, once you make the decision on the flap of a certain color being poked inside the flap of a second color, everything is fixed. You will see that play out in the instructions.

Pick up a blue unit with one hand and a red unit with another. We decided that a red flap would poke into a blue pocket. See Figures 5.5 and 5.6.

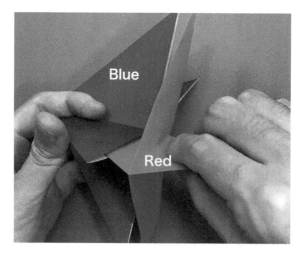

Figure 5.5.   Inserting a red unit into a blue one.

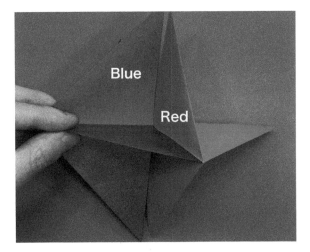

Figure 5.6. Done insertion.

Notice the direction of the red unit and the direction of the blue unit.

Now, hold the two in one hand, and pick up the third color. It is white in our example. Where this unit faces and how it connects to the other two is set by the first step. Since one flap of red is covered up, the next flap must cover up white. Using that same type of reasoning, since a blue flap covers up a red flap, its next flap must be covered up by the white flap. See Figure 5.7.

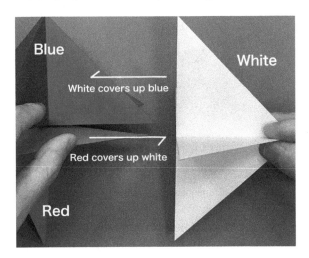

Figure 5.7. Relationship among units.

Figure 5.8 shows the start of the insertion of the white unit.

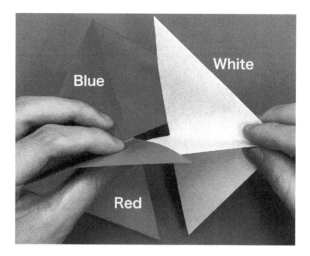

Figure 5.8.   Inserting a white unit.

Figure 5.9 shows the third piece in place. Observe that it looks like the corner of a room. Notice also all three colors are meeting.

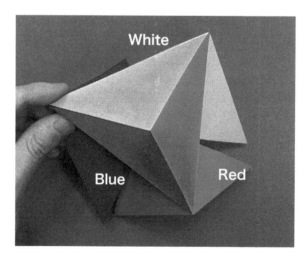

Figure 5.9.   Done inserting the third unit (white unit).

What you do now is to keep going. You have your choice of what to do next. Here, we are going to insert another red unit. It must go over a flap of the white unit and under a flap of the blue unit. Figure 5.10 shows four units in place.

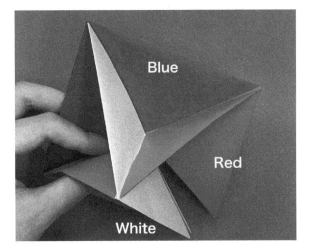

Figure 5.10. Forth unit (another red unit) in place.

Let's keep following the same rules: blue covers up red, red covers up white and white covers up blue. See Figure 5.11 and 5.12.

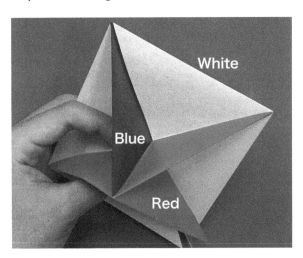

Figure 5.11. Fifth unit (another white unit) in place.

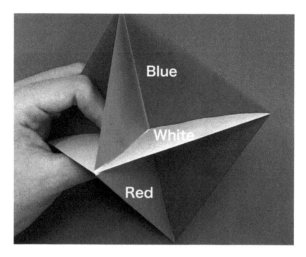

Figure 5.12.   Sixth unit (another blue unit) in place.

Look at Figure 5.13 to see the final model. Check out that your model is correctly assembled: all the inner corners must have exactly three colors. The model is fairly robust. That is, it does stay together well.

Figure 5.13.   Final model of waterbomb ornament.

King David Crown

It may be that Laura Kruskal did not call her crowns *modulars*, but we think they deserve the name. The first step is to make the unit.

Orient the paper in landscape mode: long sides on top and bottom (Figure 5.14).

Figure 5.14.   Orient paper in landscape mode.

Start to make a book fold: short side to short side, but just make a pinch at the top (Figure 5.15).

Figure 5.15.   Pinch mark in the middle at the top.

Now make diagonal folds, pivoting at that pinch, the left and the right top edges line up with the line through the center indicated by the pinch. (There is not a complete crease line at the center: just the pinch mark but it should be enough of a landmark for you to make the diagonal folds.) See Figure 5.16.

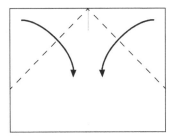

Figure 5.16.   Diagonal folds pivoting at the top pinch.

Your model should look like Figure 5.17.

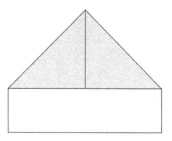

Figure 5.17. Result of the two diagonal folds.

Fold the bottom edge to meet the edges of the diagonal folds. See Figure 5.18.

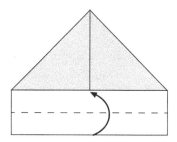

Figure 5.18. Next valley fold.

Roll over the folded edge at the bottom. This makes a crease at the edges of the diagonal folds. The folded material lies over the diagonal folds, holding them down. See Figure 5.19.

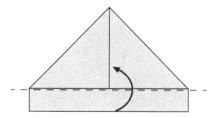

Figure 5.19. Roll over the folded edge at the bottom.

Figure 5.20 shows the result.

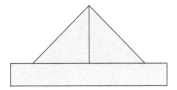

Figure 5.20. Result of rolling over the folded edge at the bottom.

Now unfold the last two folds. See Figure 5.21.

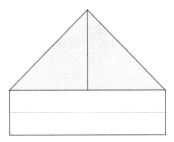

Figure 5.21. Result of unfolding the last two folds.

This is the unit. Make three more units! Then, arrange the four units on shown in Figure 5.22. This is where you would make adaptations for different size heads!

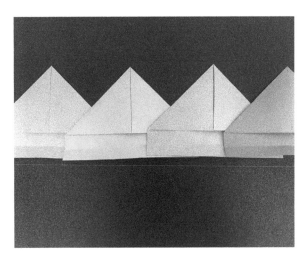

Figure 5.22. Arranging the four units horizontally.

Now lock them together by refolding the bottom two folds. See Figure 5.23.

Figure 5.23.   Locking the units together by refolding the bottom two folds.

The challenge now is to form the Crown by bending around the unit on the left and connecting it to the unit on the right and then attaching the two. It can be helpful to use paper clips at the places where the units are connected. See Figure 5.24.

Figure 5.24.   Paper clip to keep the two units together.

You may need to partially unroll—unfold—the two folds. Figure 5.25 shows both units are partially unfolded, and the right unit is inserted into the left unit. Alternatively, you can try to thread the one end into the other.

Figure 5.25. Inserting the right most unit into the left most unit.

Remove any paper clips. See Figure 5.26.

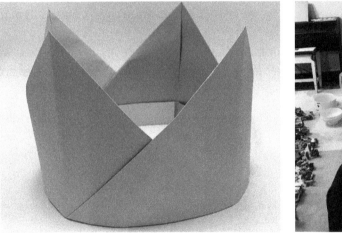 

Figure 5.26. Final model of the King David Crown, with Alexander, folder and model.

Explanations

To repeat: the unit pieces for a modular origami model generally have what are called *pockets* and *pokes* or *pockets and tabs.* The part of the unit that serves as a poke is inserted into the part of another unit that serves as a pocket. In the waterbomb ornament, each flap is both a pocket (when opened up) and a poke.

Each unit has four so there are 24 pockets and 24 pokes, but there is no need to think about all 24 at one time.

Six is not the smallest number of units possible for an origami modular. Our second book, **More Origami with Explanations**, describes the Ninja Star, which has two units. Still, many modular are made up of six units. For example, each cube for Paul Jackson's Cubes, also described in our second book, has six units. We will take some time talking about the relationships of the units.

Six units is the result of a basic characteristic of space. Space is three dimensional and there are two units for each dimension. What is meant by three dimensional? Any point in space can be defined by three distances from a fixed point. In contrast, all the points in a plane such as a flat piece of paper are specified by two numbers from an agreed upon fixed point, called the origin. Our recommendation for the waterbomb ornament is to use three sets of two units each, with both units in a set the same color. Each pair of units of the same color faces each other and is *not* locked together. Two pieces of different colors do interact and do so consistently. Each unit is connected to four of the other five units. The one left out is the unit of the same color. Assuming the colors are red, blue and white, the pattern can be red covers white; white covers blue; and blue covers red.

You know the waterbomb modular is assembled correctly if you can see all three colors displayed as the inner corner of a box or room, where the pieces are perpendicular. See Figure 5.27.

Figure 5.27.　Pieces are combined perpendicular.

There are eight identical corners like this. Imagine yourself inside a cube looking at the eight corners.

To calculate the size of the waterbomb ornament, which we can define to be the distance from point to opposite point, consider the following. Hold a unit (a waterbomb base) as shown in Figure 5.28.

Figure 5.28. Holding the waterbomb base ornament.

The distance from the center point to the vertices is the length of one of the initial book folds. This means that it is one-half the side of the square of paper. The size of the ornaments twice that which means that it is the length of the side of the square. We can confirm this by unfolding the unit. See Figure 5.29.

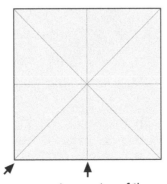

vertex of the ornament   center of the ornament

Figure 5.29. Unfolded unit indicating the position of one of the vertices of the model and its center.

The crown also has parts of unit pieces inside parts of unit pieces. However, the connections are made by laying the pieces on top of each other and restoring the folds. The last step, connecting the first to the last, is a challenge, which is the case with practically all modulars.

The crown is adaptable to different size heads, which is an essential attribute of the model.

Enhancements and Next Steps

We have suggested using three colors and standard kami for the waterbomb ornament, but after you are comfortable putting the model together, consider other possibilities. Fancy paper, such as foil, can produce lovely models. One possibility is to use the fancy paper for just one or two of the units.

You can change the Crown by putting a rim on the outside. This is done by connecting the two ends to show the rim instead of keeping it on the inside. See Figure 5.30.

Figure 5.30.   King David Crown (rim out the outside).

This crown is an appropriate model to focus on to make your own variations. We will describe one variation in Chapter 7. You certainly can use interesting paper and/or print out designs and messages on computer paper and use those for your units.

Chapter 7 focuses on the Flapping Bird and the Crane, probably the most famous origami models.

Exercises and Explorations

1. Research online to read about Jeannine Mosely's massive constructions such as her Menger's Sponge.
2. As an exercise going back and forth between 2D and 3D, calculate the angles for the ornament.
3. For Waterbomb ornament, what happens if you do not follow the pattern of covering up colors? Example: blue covers red, white covers red and white covers blue.
4. Advanced: Calculate the volume of the octahedron made with the 12 corners of the Waterbomb ornament. Do some research on how to calculate the volume of an octahedron.

Chapter 6

Flapping Bird and Crane

Background

The models for this chapter are the Flapping Bird and the Crane. The folding procedures start off the same. Figure 6.1 shows the flapping bird. The Flapping Bird is an action model: you can make the wings flap.

Figure 6.1. Flapping Bird.

Figure 6.2 shows the Crane.

Figure 6.2.   Crane.

As was indicated in Chapter 1, Jeanine's first experience with origami was learning the Flapping Bird, but we agree with Lillian Oppenheimer that it should not be the first model that a person new to origami learns. Being able to fold the Flapping Bird is the official benchmark defining an intermediate folder at the OrigamiUSA convention. However, you are ready for it now. Both the models start off with the *Bird Base*, which is the start of many models, and not just birds.

You will learn two methods of folding the *Bird Base*, one starting with the *Preliminary Base* (aka *Square Base*) and the other featuring folding and unfolding and then a collapse all at once into the *Bird Base*.

The Exercises and Exploration section includes the challenge to investigate the custom of making 1000 cranes for a cause or a special gift.

SUPPLIES

Flapping Bird & Crane

Some students enjoy folding small models, especially this one, but we recommend starting off with larger, say 10-inch kami paper squares for each. Light, solid colors make it easier to see the crease lines. Have smaller and smaller sizes available for follow-up folding.

Instructions

The first step in making the Flapping Bird or the Crane is to make a *Bird Base*. We describe two different methods for making a Bird Base.

Method 1: Preliminary Base using petal fold

One of the reasons for the name "Preliminary Base" is that it is preliminary to making the *Bird Base*. Please make a *Preliminary Base* (aka *Square Base*) as was shown for the Star Basket in Chapter 2. You make two book folds on the white side and two diagonal folds on the color side. Collapse the paper. If you need more detail directions along with figures, you can go back to Chapter 2. See Figure 6.3 which shows the *Preliminary Base*. The closed point is at the top. Make sure the model is *balanced*: two flaps on each side.

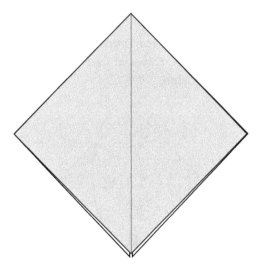

Figure 6.3.   Preliminary Base.

The next two steps are to make preparation folds on each side by taking the bottom part of the flap on the right and the flap on the left and folding it to the center. You will be folding the cut edges to the center. This is "preparation" as you did for the squash folds in Chapter 2, but you will NOT be making squash folds, but something called a *petal fold*. See Figure 6.4.

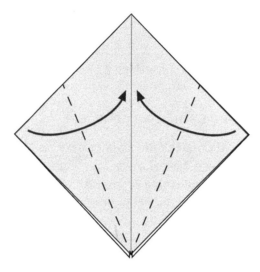

Figure 6.4.   Preparation folds for a petal fold.

Figure 6.5 shows the results of the preparation folds, and indication for the next fold, also a preparation fold. This next fold is to fold the top point down on top of the two folds you just made.

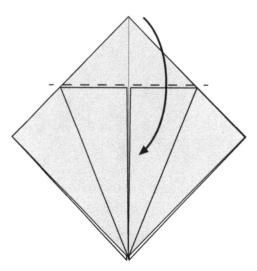

Figure 6.5.   Result of the preparation folds and next preparation.

Figure 6.6 shows the result of folding the top point down.

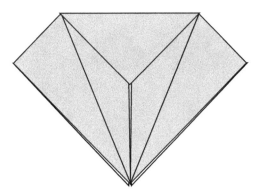

Figure 6.6. Result of folding the top point down.

Now unfold the top point and also unfold the two folds that were folded into the center. Figure 6.7 shows the result.

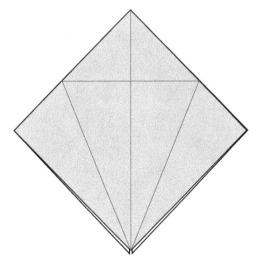

Figure 6.7. Unfold the top point and the preparation folds.

You will now make what is called a petal fold. This is done by lifting up one layer and then folding on the crease lines made. However, you will be changing the sense (valley to mountain) of some of the folds. It is a multi-step process and we show how the process using photos. See Figures 6.8–6.11.

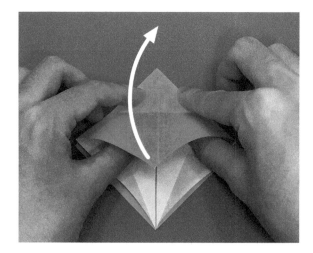

Figure 6.8.   Lifting up one layer.

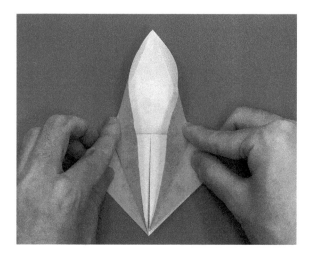

Figure 6.9.   Petal fold in process.

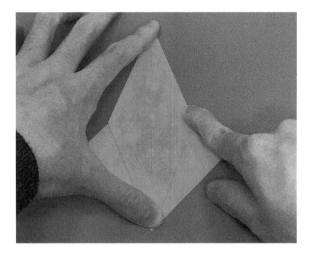

Figure 6.10.   Reinforce the crease lines.

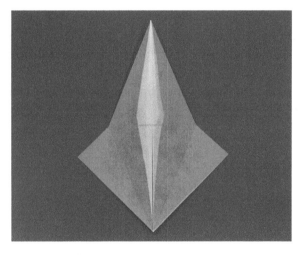

Figure 6.11.   Done petal folds.

Figure 6.12 shows a diagram showing one complete petal fold and the instruction to turn the model over.

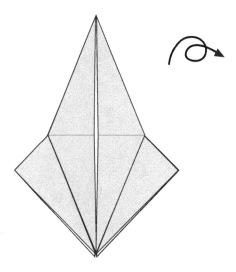

Figure 6.12.   Petal fold and turning the model over.

Turn the model over as indicated in the last figure. The model looks different because of what was done on the other side, but essentially the procedure is to repeat what was just done: preparation folds and then a petal fold. We repeat the directions.

Figure 6.13 shows the model on the other side and valley lines directing you to make the preparation folds.

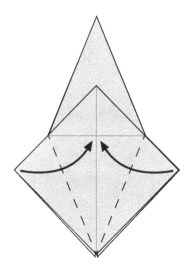

Figure 6.13.   Model turned over and valley folds as preparation folds.

Figure 6.14 shows the results of the preparation folds. Notice the whole model is narrower now. The instructions are to fold the smaller triangle down to lie on top of the preparation folds.

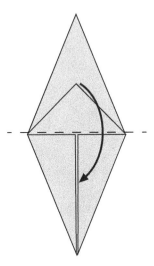

Figure 6.14. Complete preparation folds.

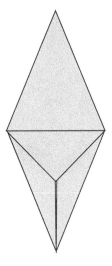

Figure 6.15. Result of folding the top point down.

Unfold the top and the two preparation folds on the sides and make a petal fold. Figures 6.16–6.18 show the process.

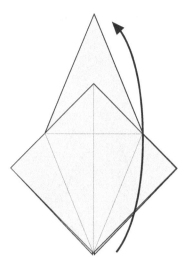

Figure 6.16.   Bring the bottom to the top.

Figure 6.17.   Petal fold in process.

Figure 6.18. Reinforce the creases.

This is a *Bird Base*. More accurately, this is a *Bird Base with two points up*. See Figure 6.19.

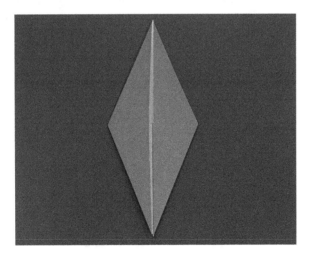

Figure 6.19. Bird base with two points up.

We now show a different way to produce a bird base.

Method 2: Folding and unfolding and collapse to Bird Base all-at-once

An alternative to the petal fold method is what can be called "the all-at-once" method. It starts by making the folds for the *Preliminary Base/Square Base* but do not do the collapse. We will give an accelerated sequence of these initial steps. Place paper with white side up as shown in Figure 6.20.

Figure 6.20.   White side up.

The next steps, indicated in Figure 6.21, shows the location of two book folds.

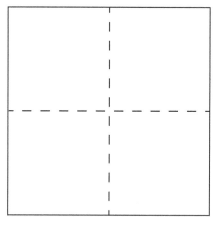

Figure 6.21.   Two book folds.

Turn the model over and, as shown in Figure 6.22, make two diagonal (point to opposite point) folds:

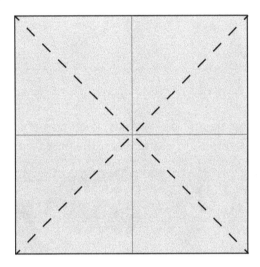

Figure 6.22. Two diagonal folds on color side.

This is when you could do the collapse to the Preliminary base, but, instead, turn the model back over to the white side.

The next set of steps is to make what we will describe as eight partial folds. (We will use several figures to show you what to do.) At each corner vertex, for each of the two edges ending at that vertex, fold the edge to the diagonal, but only crease to the nearest fold line. There will be two folds at each corner for eight folds in all. This set of folds is indicated in Figure 6.23.

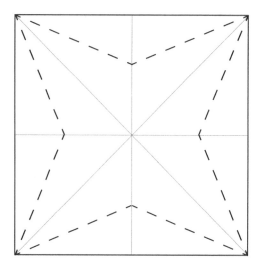

Figure 6.23.   Valley folds for eight partial folds.

Here is a way to make the partial folds. Restore one of the diagonal folds. Figure 6.24 shows the result and indication of the next step.

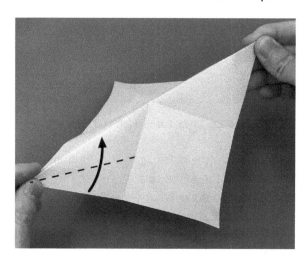

Figure 6.24.   Restore one diagonal fold.

You accomplish the partial fold by folding one layer on the left side to the top, folded edge. Only crease to the first crease line. See Figure 6.25.

Figure 6.25. Crease the partial fold on the left side.

Unfold and repeat on the right side. See Figure 6.26.

Figure 6.26. Crease the partial fold on the right side.

Turn the model over and repeat, making two partial folds against the same diagonal. Now unfold the diagonal fold. Figure 6.27 shows the result.

Figure 6.27.   Four partial folds creased and unfolded diagonal fold.

Notice that there are four partial folds made. To make the rest, make (restore) the other diagonal fold as indicated Figure 6.28.

Figure 6.28.   Restore another diagonal fold.

Repeat the last steps, making four partial folds in all. Remember to just fold one layer. You will be making 2 on one side and then turn the paper over to do 2 more. Unfold the diagonal. Figure 6.29 shows the result.

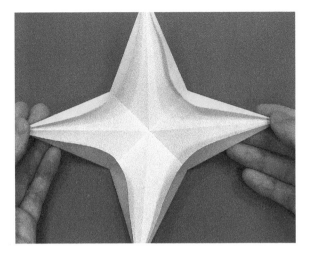

Figure 6.29. Eight partial folds creased and unfolded diagonal folds.

The paper can now be collapsed into the *Bird Base*. Reinforce the diagonals and the book folds. Then reinforce the partial folds. The photos show the process, starting with Figure 6.30 in which you have reinforces the partial folds.

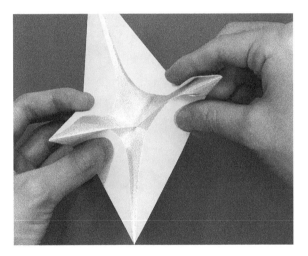

Figure 6.30. Reinforce partial folds.

Now press on the book folds, as if you were collapsing the model into the *square base*, as shown in Figures 6.31 and 6.32.

Figure 6.31. Collapsing in process.

Figure 6.32. Done collapsing.

Figure 6.33 shows the complete Bird Base.

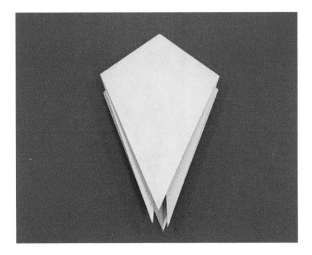

Figure 6.33. Bird Base.

Since we want the front and back flaps up, do the step indicated in Figures 6.34 and 6.35.

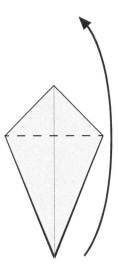

Figure 6.34. Bring the bottom point to up.

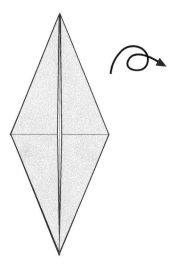

Figure 6.35.   Done on the front and turn over the model.

Figure 6.36 shows one point turned up. The instructions are to repeat. See Figure 6.37.

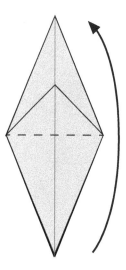

Figure 6.36.   Bring the bottom point to up.

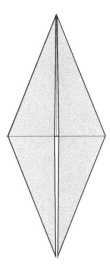

Figure 6.37. Done on the back.

You now have seen two methods for making a Bird Base, the petal fold and the all-at-once collapse. Jeanine finds the all-at-once method easier to be accurate, but there are some other models, for example, making a bird as part of a larger model, where the petal fold method is required. One of these is the Traditional Frog, the subject of the next chapter, so it is a good technique to master. Practice both and then you can choose. We now continue, first, with the procedure for the Flapping Bird and then for the Crane.

FOR TEACHERS

We ask the students which way they liked and it was a good way to engage them in thinking about folding.

Make a Flapping Bird

After making a Bird Base, the next step to make the Flapping Bird is to form the neck-and-head. This will be done by an *inside reverse fold*. (NOTE: the term reverse fold without the "inside" adjective also is used for what we describe here. There also is an *outside reverse fold* in which, as you could guess, the folds go outside. You can find examples of this in our **More Origami with Explanations** book, the *Kissy Fish* chapter, and other sources.) Look at Figure 6.38. You will see a valley fold on the right. This is a preparation fold for the bird neck and is "to taste". Look at the result shown in Figure 6.39 and make this fold.

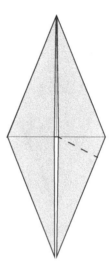

Figure 6.38.   Preparation fold for inside reverse fold.

Figure 6.39 shows the result of the preparation fold. The preparation fold makes creases with two layers of paper.

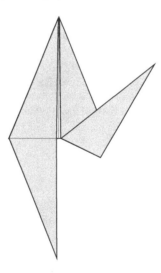

Figure 6.39.   Result of the preparation fold.

Now unfold. The next step is to open up the paper as shown in Figure 6.40 and refold on the same lines.

Figure 6.40. Open up the paper.

You will be changing one crease line from mountain to valley (reversing it) and refolding the other crease to remain a valley fold. See Figures 6.41 and 6.42.

Figure 6.41. Inside reverse fold in process.

Figure 6.42.   Result of the inside reverse fold.

Repeat on the left for the bird tail: make a preparation fold as shown in Figures 6.43 and 6.44.

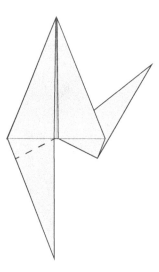

Figure 6.43.   Another preparation fold.

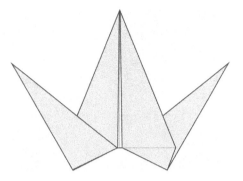

Figure 6.44. Result of the preparation fold.

Then unfold and finish the reverse fold. See Figures 6.45 and 6.46.

Figure 6.45. Inside reverse fold in process.

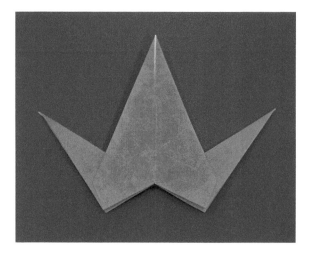

Figure 6.46.   Result of the inside reverse fold.

Sequences of steps with preparation folds and then reversing some of the crease lines are common in origami. The "inside" indicates that a portion of the paper is pushed inside.

The head is formed by another reverse fold. See Figures 6.47 and 6.48. This also is "to taste."

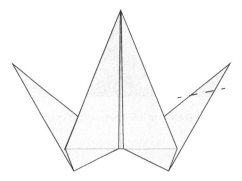

Figure 6.47.   Another preparation fold for head.

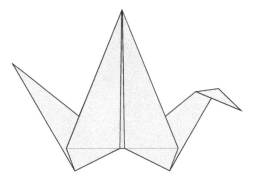

Figure 6.48. Result of the preparation fold.

Unfold, open up the layers, and reverse the folds. See Figures 6.49 and 6.50.

Figure 6.49. Inside reverse fold in process.

Figure 6.50.   Result of the inside reverse fold.

The two center flaps are the wings. These can be shaped into a gentle curve using a pencil. See Figure 6.51.

Figure 6.51.   Shaping the wing with a pen.

The bird flaps its wings by holding the chest of the bird and pulling the tail as shown in Figure 6.52 and pulling the tail.

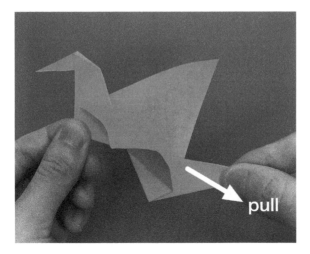

Figure 6.52.   Pulling the tail to flap the wings.

Make a Crane

We now describe how to make a Crane. It is very similar to the Flapping Bird. We start again with a *Bird Base.* You can use the petal method or the collapse-all-at-once method.

The crane is made by narrowing the model. Starting from the *Bird Base*, narrow (skinny) the model by making the valley folds indicated in Figures 6.53 and 6.54.

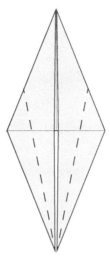

Figure 6.53.   Valley folds to narrow the model.

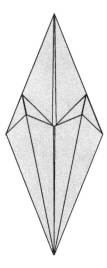

Figure 6.54.   Result of the narrowing the model process on one side.

Turn over the model and repeat the same procedure. See Figures 6.55 and 6.56.

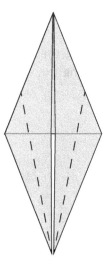

Figure 6.55.   Valley folds to narrow the model.

Figure 6.56. Result of the narrowing the model process on the other side.

The tail and the neck-and-head now can be formed as was shown for the Flapping Bird. However, we will show another way. Perform a *minor miracle* by flipping over the flaps in the front and the back. See Figures 6.57 and 6.58.

Figure 6.57. Flapping over one flap (minor miracle in process).

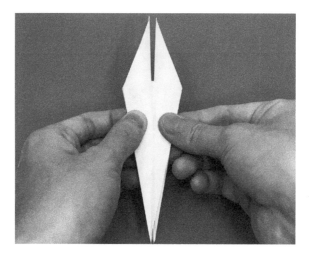

Figure 6.58.   Result of the minor miracle.

Now fold the flap as indicated in Figures 6.59 and 6.60. Do not reinforce this crease.

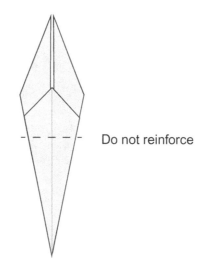

Do not reinforce

Figure 6.59.   Valley fold after the minor miracle.

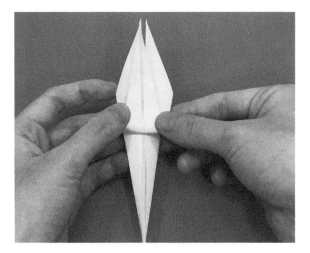

Figure 6.60.   Result of the valley fold, but not reinforced.

Flip the model over to repeat in the back. Again: Do not reinforce this fold. See Figure 6.61.

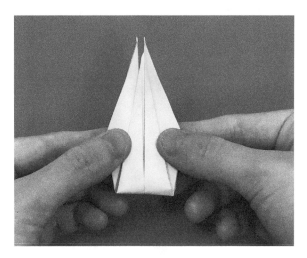

Figure 6.61.   Result of the valley fold, but not reinforced.

Flip the flaps back—undo the minor miracle folds front and back. The result is shown in Figure 6.62.

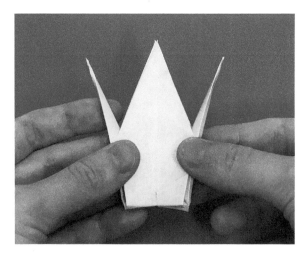

Figure 6.62.   Undo the minor miracle folds front and back.

The minor miracle folding produces what the reverse folding would have produced. However, you will need to adjust the neck-and-head and the tail. This is why we said not to reinforce the folds. See Figure 6.63.

Figure 6.63.   Adjust the neck and tail and fold the bottom parts.

Finally, make a head by another reverse fold. See Figures 6.64 and 6.65.

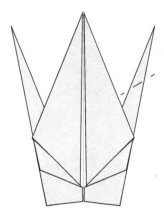

Figure 6.64. Reverse fold for the head.

Figure 6.65. Result of the reverse fold.

It is a common practice to string groups of cranes together, in which case they are kept flat. However, it is possible to make a crane more three dimensional. Grab the wings and pull out. See Figure 6.66.

Figure 6.66.   Transform to three dimensional model by grabbing the wings and pulling them out.

TIP

To make it easier to make a crane three dimensional, some people recommend that they put their thumbs at the corners of where the middle section meets the wings and pull from there. It also helps avoid ripping the paper as you pull.

You also can inflate the model by blowing into the hole at the bottom as we did for Waterbomb. See Figure 6.67.

Figure 6.67.   Hole to blow into.

Explanations

The two methods of making a bird base produce slightly different crease patterns. See Figures 6.68 and 6.69.

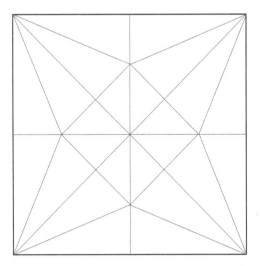

Figure 6.68.   Crease pattern of Preliminary Base and Petal fold method.

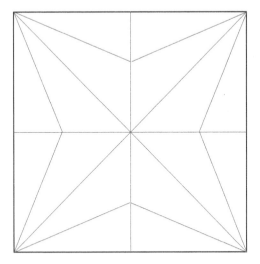

Figure 6.69.   Crease pattern of all-at-once method.

However, the difference goes away when lifting the front and back layers. See Figures 6.70 and 6.71.

Figure 6.70.   Model made by all-at-once method.

Figure 6.71.   Lifting up the front and back to make the same crease pattern as Preliminary Base and Petal fold method.

The two methods demonstrate what is going on with the Petal fold: the sense of certain fold lines are changed. In contrast, the all-at-once approach makes the partial folds be the sense required for the collapse. Practice doing both approaches and observe what happens.

Let's calculate the wingspan of the Flapping Bird. Look at Figure 6.72. This is the crease pattern for the Bird. Focus on the lower left square. It is the *Bird Base* and does *not* have lines for the head-and-front and tail of the Flapping Bird.

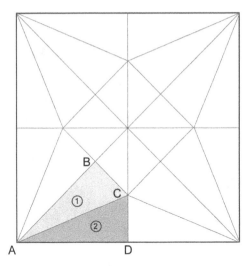

Figure 6.72. Two highlighted triangles with labels.

The length of the wing is from A to B. The triangle indicated by the number 1 is congruent (same size and shape) to the triangle indicated by the number 2 based on the folding. Using the petal fold method, the preparation fold we described has the cut edges folded to the center as shown in Figure 6.73. Naming triangles by the vertices, triangle 1 is ABC and triangle 2 is ADC. The length of A to B is the same as the length from A to D. This is 1/2 the side of the original square. Therefore, using S for the size of the original square, the length of one wing is S/2. The length of two wings would be two times S/2. We haven't been concerned with the thickness of the paper before, but it seems appropriate now. The wing-span: tip to tip would be plus the thicknesses of the four layers of paper making up the body of the bird.

Figure 6.73.   Folding the side over to the center.

Enhancements and Next Steps

Many models have a *Bird Base* or partial *Bird Base* folded from part of the paper. As we mentioned earlier, these models may make use of petal folds. For example, inspired by Laura Kruskal's King David Crown (see Chapter 5) and the Business Card Frog (see Chapter 1), we made this variation. (Others may have done this as well. Let's call it Birds on a Crown.) Orient a piece of copier paper so the short sides are at the top and bottom and proceed with diagonal folds as with the frog. See Figure 6.74.

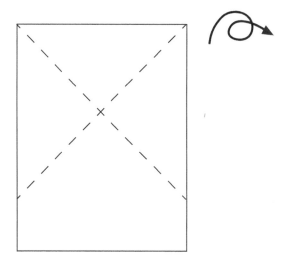

Figure 6.74.   Diagonal folds and turning over the model.

Turn the paper over and, again like the frog, fold the top to the bottom of the X making a crease going through the middle of the X. See Figure 6.75.

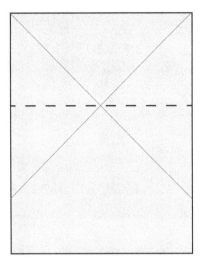

Figure 6.75. Valley fold at the middle of X.

Collapse into a waterbomb base. See Figures 6.76 and 6.77.

Figure 6.76. Collapsing the valley fold.

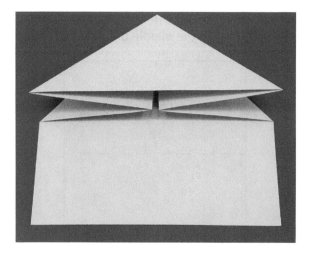

Figure 6.77.   Done the collapse and waterbomb base.

Now take the flap on the right and squash it. Figures 6.78–6.81 show the preparation fold and then the squash.

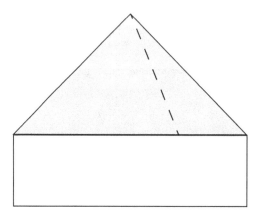

Figure 6.78.   Preparation fold for the squash.

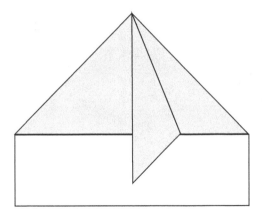

Figure 6.79. Result of the preparation fold.

Figure 6.80. Squash fold in process.

Figure 6.81.   Result of the squash fold.

Now, make a petal fold out of the squash. Figures 6.82 and 6.83 show the preparation folds.

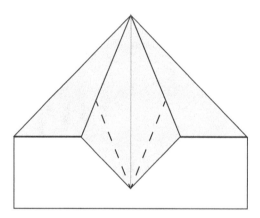

Figure 6.82.   Preparation folds for petal fold.

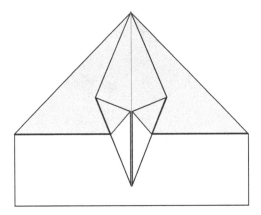

Figure 6.83. Result of the preparation folds.

Unfold the preparation folds and move the center up. See Figures 6.84–6.86.

Figure 6.84. Start petal fold.

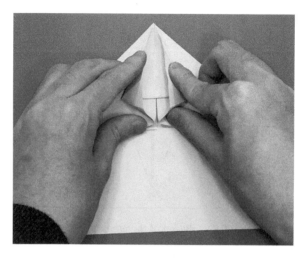

Figure 6.85.   Petal fold in process.

Figure 6.86.   Result of the petal fold.

Fold the left side of this long flap over and now do the same with the flap on the left: preparation fold, squash, preparation folds, petal fold.

Proceeding as you did for the Flapping Bird, use two reverse folds to form a head and chest out of the flap on the right and use one reverse fold to form a tail out of the long flap on the left. See Figures 6.87–6.90.

Figure 6.87. Two petal folds on right and left side and smooth side facing up.

Figure 6.88. Adjusting the neck position.

Figure 6.89.   Result of the adjustment of neck and tail.

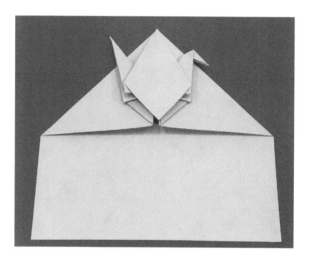

Figure 6.90.   Result of the inside reverse fold for the head.

Now use this as the unit: make three more and put them together as described in Chapter 5.

The next chapter features the *Traditional Frog*. We also point out common features in the crease patterns of the major bases.

Exercises and Explorations

1. There are several distinct aspects to the cultural significance of folding cranes to be investigated. These include:
   a. Significance of the crane in Japan;
   b. Different legends and stories about folding 1000 cranes, called Senbazuru;
   c. Specific story of Sadako Sasaki, exposed to radiation from the atomic bombing of Hiroshima.
2. Folding 1000 or some larger number of cranes or something else is a common activity for causes. In Spring 2019, an organization against gun violence collected orange cranes for a demonstration. Origami elephants of various designs were collected for a campaign against the poaching and killing of elephants in Africa. Investigate if any similar efforts are going on in your community.
3. Study your Crane model and compare with your Flapping Bird model. Why doesn't the crane flap?
4. Using the all-at-once method, show that the two triangles in the wingspan calculation are congruent.
5. Calculate the wingspan for a Crane. Hint: take the Bird Base diagram and add the crease lines for folds that narrow the model. Use these folds to add the crease lines that start the wings.
6. Do some research on models created from a *Bird Base*?

Chapter 7

Traditional Frog on Lily Pad

Background

The model for this chapter is the Traditional Frog, which can be made to jump like the Business Card Frog, or blown up as shown in Figure 7.1. The frog is shown on a Lily Pad made from a paper dinner napkin.

Figure 7.1.   Traditional Frog on Lily Pad.

The start of the folding for this model is called the *Frog Base*. We will use this chapter to go over the *Kite*, *Fish*, *Bird* and *Frog* bases, and show the crease patterns. Peter Engel pointed out relationships, most notably a progression, in the sequence of crease patterns for these bases.

Instructions

Frog Base

The Frog base starts off with a *Square Base*, also called a *Preliminary Base*, and is the same start as the Flapping Bird and the Crane, when made using the petal fold method. See Figures 7.2 and 7.3.

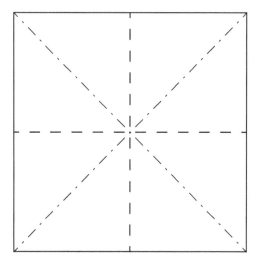

Figure 7.2. Crease patterns for Square Base.

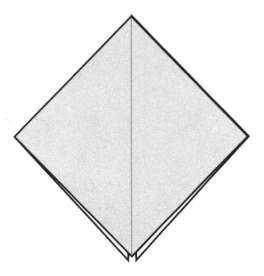

Figure 7.3. Square base.

Notice that there are four flaps: two flaps on the right side and two flaps on the left side. The next series of steps consists of operations each done four times, once for each flap. It helps to keep the flaps balanced: two to a side.

The first set of steps is making squash folds. We start with one of the flaps on the right. Make a preparation fold as indicated on the diagram. See Figure 7.4.

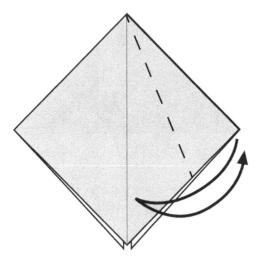

Figure 7.4. Square base with preparation fold line indicated.

Unfold and squash as shown in Figures 7.5 and 7.6.

Figure 7.5.   Squash fold in process.

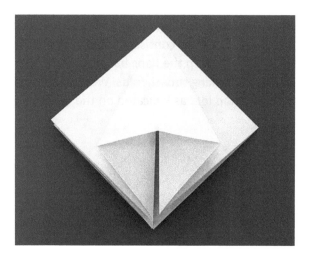

Figure 7.6.   Result of the squash fold.

Move on to the next flap by making the fold indicated in Figure 7.7. This provides room for you to do the next squash fold.

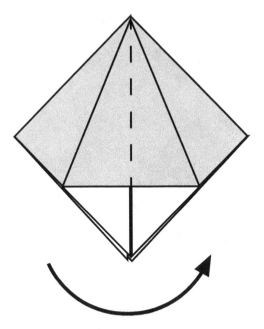

Figure 7.7. Minor miracle to provide room to do the next squash fold.

Make the preparation fold on the flap on the left. See Figure 7.8.

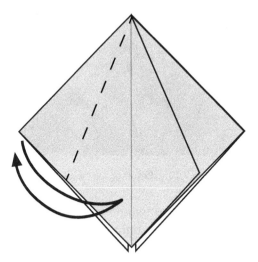

Figure 7.8. Preparation fold line indicated.

Unfold and squash. The result is shown in Figures 7.9 and 7.10.

Figure 7.9.   Squash fold in process.

Figure 7.10.   Result of the squash fold.

Turn the model over and make two more squash folds. The procedures are the same. Make one squash on both right and left sides. Figure 7.11 shows the result of the all squash folds.

Figure 7.11. Result of the all squash folds.

Also, make sure the flaps are balanced, meaning four layers to a side. See Figure 7.12.

Figure 7.12. Four flaps on both sides.

The next set of operations are petal folds. This is similar to what we showed in the chapter on the Flapping Bird and the Crane in the first method for making a *Bird Base*. We will repeat the instructions.

The preparation for petal folds involves folding one layer over on the lower right and one layer over on the lower left. Figure 7.13 show where the preparation folds are, and Figure 7.14 shows the result of the two folds.

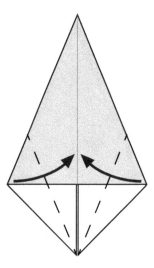

Figure 7.13.   Valley folds for preparation folds.

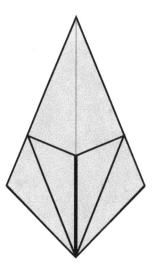

Figure 7.14.   Result of the preparation folds.

Now complete the petal fold by slightly unfolding the last two folds and pulling up the middle and then pressing it down so that the raw edges can lie flat. You are re-using folds, changing the sense of folds and making new folds. See Figures 7.15–7.21.

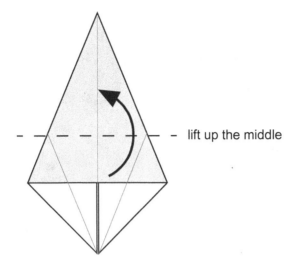

lift up the middle

Figure 7.15.   Lifting up for petal fold.

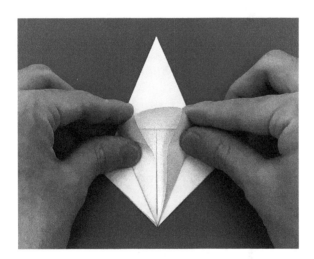

Figure 7.16.   Start petal fold.

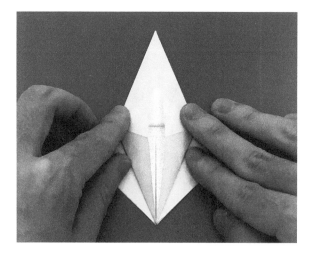

Figure 7.17.   Petal fold in process.

Figure 7.18.   Reinforce the top creases.

The next photo shows the completed petal.

Figure 7.19. Result of the petal fold.

Repeat this process three more times. We need to do minor miracle to provide room for the next petal fold.

Figure 7.20. Minor miracle to provide room to do the next petal fold.

Figure 7.21. Place to make another petal fold.

After you make all four petal folds, you will have a Frog base as shown in Figure 7.22.

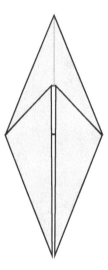

Figure 7.22. Model after completing all the petal folds.

The Bird Base requires two petal folds and the Frog Base requires four. The Frog base has radial symmetry; that is: not just bilateral symmetry on each side, but the same shape each quarter turn when lifted up off the table and viewed on end as shown in Figure 7.23.

Figure 7.23. Radial symmetry seen from the top.

Traditional Frog

The next set of folds is to skinny each of the lower flaps. Adjust the model so that a smooth side is facing you and the flaps are balanced. This means that a smooth side is facing the back, also. See Figures 7.24 and 7.25.

Figure 7.24. Minor miracle to get a smooth side.

Figure 7.25. Smooth side facing up.

Fold in each side as indicated in Figures 7.26 and 7.27.

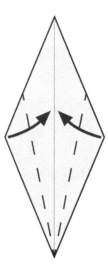

Figure 7.26. Valley fold to make the model narrower.

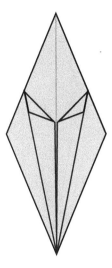

Figure 7.27. Result of the previous folds.

Adjust the model by doing minor miracle (flipping the flaps in front and in back) to get to the next smooth side and repeat. Do this a total of four times. See Figure 7.28 for a diagram of the result so far.

Figure 7.28. Result of the narrowing process.

Take one layer on the left and move it over to the right. Turn the model over and repeat the same procedure (Figures 7.29 and 7.30). See the result in Figure 7.31. Make sure that the flaps on both sides are balanced meaning that four layers on each side.

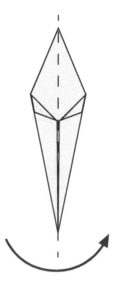

Figure 7.29.   Minor miracle.

Figure 7.30.   Minor miracle in process.

Figure 7.31. Result of the minor miracle.

Some call this the tadpole, though there already are four potential legs. See Figure 7.32 for a photo of the model seen from the bottom.

Figure 7.32. Four potential legs.

The Frog is made by forming two front legs towards the front of the frog and two legs to the sides.

The first set of steps for the legs consist of one reverse fold for each leg, with one pair directed towards the front and the other towards the side. Figure 7.33 indicates possible placement of the preparation folds for the front legs.

The folding is *"to taste"* so use your knowledge of frogs and/or imagination to make your model.

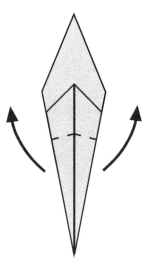

Figure 7.33.   Preparation folds for front legs.

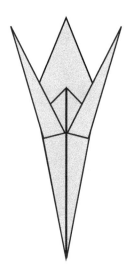

Figure 7.34.   Result of the preparation folds.

The next step is to make reverse folds in each place (Figures 7.34 and 7.35). Figures 7.36 shows the result.

Figure 7.35. Reverse fold in process.

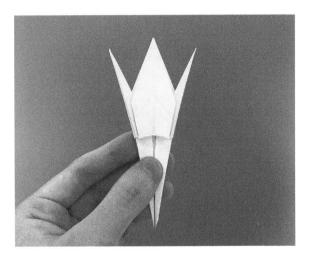

Figure 7.36. Result of the reverse folds.

Now turn the model over and make the preparation folds for the back legs (Figure 7.37). This also is "to taste." What we are calling the back legs typically are placed out to the sides and, maybe even pointing slightly forward. Figure 7.38 shows the preparation folds.

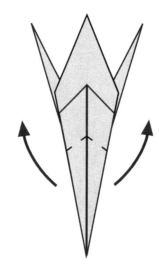

Figure 7.37.   Preparation folds for back legs.

Figure 7.38.   Result of the preparation folds.

The next step is to make reverse folds in each place (Figure 7.39). Figure 7.40 shows the result.

Figure 7.39.   Reverse fold in process.

Figure 7.40.   Result of the reverse folds.

There are alternate approaches to the final shaping of the legs. The goal in all cases is to put in two joints in each leg. You can use inside reverse folds or simply bend the paper or a combination. See Figures 7.41–7.44.

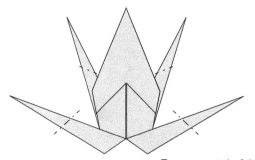

Four mountain folds

Figure 7.41.   Mountain folds to make the first joint.

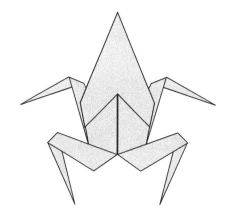

Figure 7.42.   Result of the mountain folds.

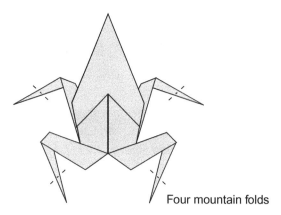

Four mountain folds

Figure 7.43.   Mountain folds to make the second joint.

Figure. 7.44. Result of the mountain folds.

Figure 7.45 shows the result of bending the paper.

Figure 7.45. Result of bending the legs.

It is possible to make the frog jump by running your finger on the back as was done with the Business Card Frog. However, an alternative that our students enjoy is to inflate the frog by blowing into the hole. See Figures 7.46 and 7.47.

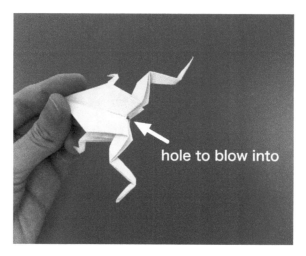

Figure 7.46. Hole to blow into.

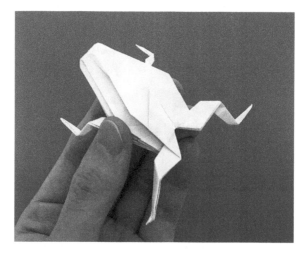

Figure 7.47. Final model of Traditional Frog.

Inflating the frog takes away the jumping capability. We postpone showing a picture until we show you how to make a lily pad.

Lily Pad

Frogs (sometimes) are on lily pads in ponds. Take a napkin and unfold it. See Figure 7.48.

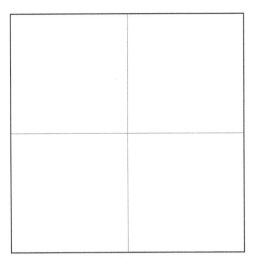

Figure 7.48. Diagram of unfolded napkin.

Figure 7.49 shows a diagram with the next set of folds indicated. We have seen this before: it is a *blintz fold*. You make a blintz fold by folding each corner to the center. The center is already marked based on the way the napkin is folded and packaged at the store. However, the napkin may not be exactly square, so fold the blintz as best you can. The flaps may overlap.

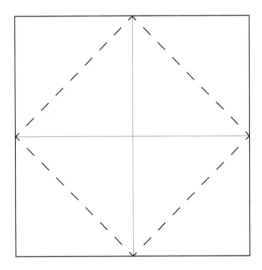

Figure 7.49. Blintz folds.

Figure 7.50 shows a diagram with the results and the next set of folds. The instruction is to repeat the blintz on what is now a smaller square.

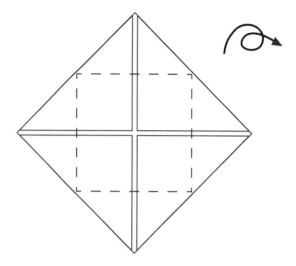

Figure 7.50.　Another blintz folds on the previous blintz folds.

Follow the directions to turn the model over and repeat with one more blintz fold. See Figure 7.51.

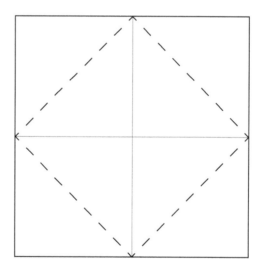

Figure 7.51.　Blintz folds on the other side.

The result is shown in Figure 7.52.

Figure 7.52. Result of the previous steps.

Summing up, you have made two complete blintz folds on one side and one complete blintz fold on the other side.

The next steps are to reach underneath and pull up the flaps. Go around and pull up flaps made by the last blintz fold on the other side (Figures 7.53–7.55).

Figure 7.53. Flap to pull up.

Figure 7.54.   Pulling up in process.

Figure 7.55.   Complete one petal.

Repeat: go around again and pull up the flaps (Figure 7.56).

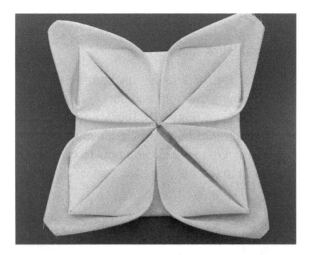

Figure 7.56. Final model of lily pad.

This produces the lily pad, which we now show in Figure 7.57 with a frog.

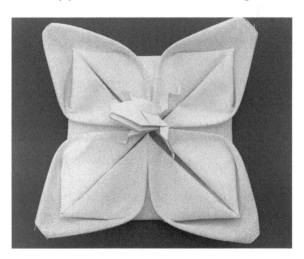

Figure 7.57. Frog on the lily pad.

Explanations

Going to 3D and Final Dimensions

The folding procedure for the Traditional Frog had the transition from 2D to 3D be in two stages: first, forming the front and back legs and secondly (and optionally) blowing up the frog as was done with the Waterbomb and Tulip.

Some of the final dimensions of the frog are dependent on the to-taste folds forming the legs. However, we can show you how to calculate the distance from the end of the frog's head to the tip of the leg, that is, we go back to the tadpole. Unfold the paper: see in Figure 7.58.

Figure 7.58.   Crease patterns after unfolding the frog.

The top of the head is the center of the paper. Each potential limb is a corner of the paper. The length is the hypotenuse of the square, which is a quarter of the paper.

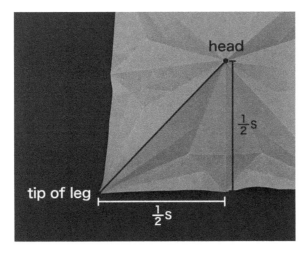

Figure 7.59. Indicating the positions of the head and the tip of leg and important lengths.

The square has size side of the original square (call this S) divided by 2. Call it $\frac{1}{2}$S. From formulas we have used before, the hypotenuse is $\sqrt{2} \times \frac{1}{2}$S. See Figure 7.59.

Patterns in Crease Patterns of Four Bases

We now invite you along to do some pattern matching, or, perhaps better described as pattern finding.

TIP

The idea of examining the crease patterns for the four bases is Peter Engel's and can be found in his book **Origami Angelfish to Zen**. We strongly recommend it for the origami models and the history.

In this book, you have seen several origami bases. These are models that are the basis of other models; that is, the first steps for other models. You have seen the Kite base for the stem and leaf for the Tulip, the Bird base for the Crane and Flapping Bird, and the Frog base for the Traditional frog shown in this chapter. There is one more base, the *Fish base*, that we describe quickly here. (See the exercises for a challenge to use the Fish base for a whale.)

The Fish base is produced by making a diagonal fold, and unfolding and then making what are called *Rabbit Ear* folds. Figures 7.60 and 7.61 indicate the first steps: fold an edge to the center line and unfold.

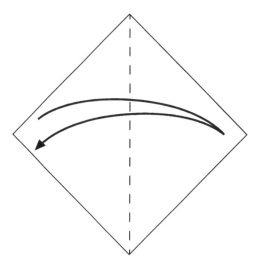

Figure 7.60.   One diagonal fold.

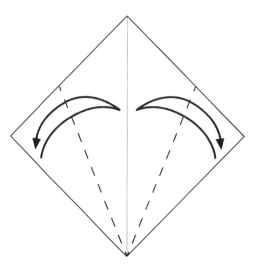

Figure 7.61.   Fold edges to the center line.

Fold the adjacent edge to the center line as indicated Figure 7.62 and unfold.

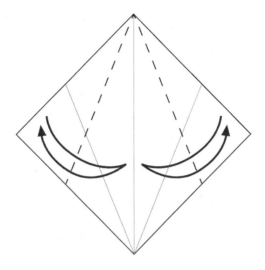

Figure 7.62. Fold the other edges to the center line.

Now, start to refold both of the folds, as indicated in Figure 7.63. This is a *Rabbit Ear.*

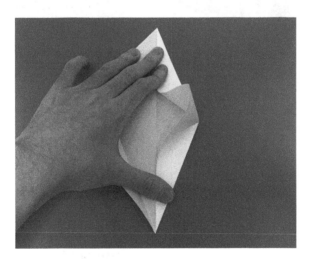

Figure 7.63. Rabbit ear.

Then fold the middle part to one side as shown in Figures 7.64 and 7.65.

Figure 7.64.   Folded rabbit ear.

Figure 7.65.   Folded rabbit ear seen from the side.

Repeat on the other side. This is the Fish base. See Figures 7.66 and 7.67.

Figure 7.66. After two rabbit ear folds.

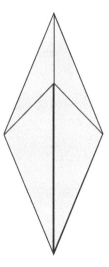

Figure 7.67. Completed Fish base.

We show the crease patterns of the four bases: Kite, Fish, Bird and Frog. The order is important. When you look at the crease patterns of the bases, try to see if there is a part that is present one or more times in each base. After all the crease patterns are presented, we will show the common part. Peter Engel calls it "the module."

The Kite base is shown in Figure 7.68. Note there is one extra line from what we made for the Tulip Stem. The Fish base is shown in Figure 7.69.

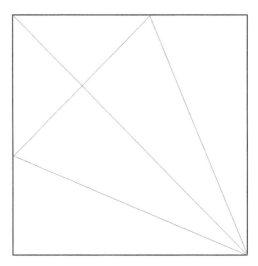

Figure 7.68.   Crease pattern of Kite base.

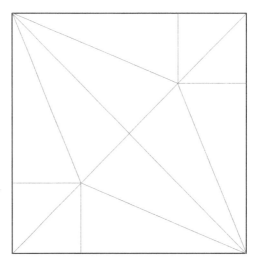

Figure 7.69.   Crease pattern of Fish base.

The Bird base folding pattern, based on petal fold method, is shown in Figure 7.70.

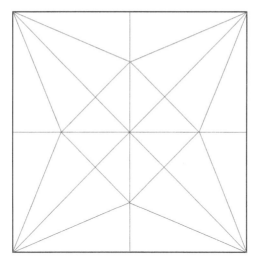

Figure 7.70. Crease pattern of Bird base.

The Frog base pattern is shown in Figure 7.71. The crease pattern shows the radial symmetry.

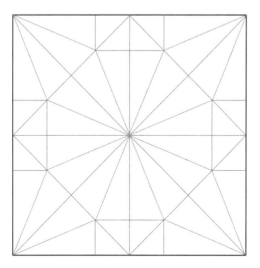

Figure 7.71. Crease pattern of Frog base.

Note: this pattern does require folding the triangle shape produced by the pedal fold down and back up. This is shown in Figure 7.72.

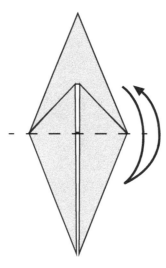

Figure 7.72.   Fold down the small triangle.

Figure 7.73 shows the module that occurs in each of the base crease patterns.

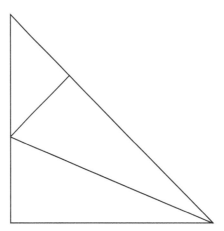

Figure 7.73.   Module that occurs in each of the base crease patterns.

Now, please examine all four patterns, shown in Figure 7.74, and see how many times the module occurs in each pattern.

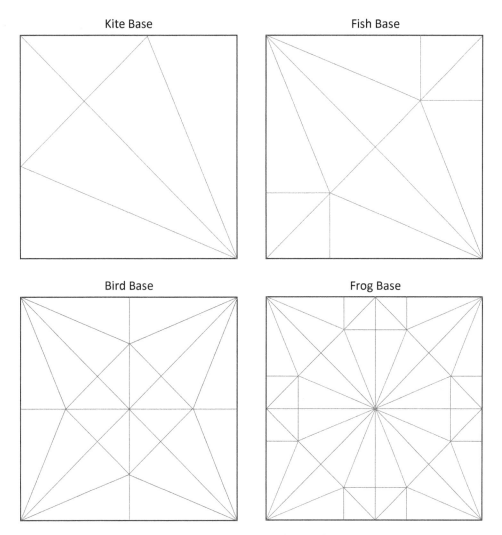

Figure 7.74. Crease patterns of the all four bases.

In fact, the module occurs

Base	Number of times module occurs
Kite	2
Fish	4
Bird	8
Frog	16

There are other patterns to notice: the Frog base is made up of four copies of the Fish base. The Bird base is made up of four copies of the Kite base.

It appears that the bases were invented in Japan as independent models. There is no evidence that this progression was part of the origins of origami. The independent inventions certainly led to beautiful origami models. However, these geometric patterns and the relationships have their own beauty.

Enhancements and Next Steps

This frog is crying out (croaking out?) for decoration. You also may try to start with the Frog base and see what models you can design. There are four flaps.

TIP FOR TEACHERS AND PARENTS

This may be an appropriate time to make a challenge to make variations to any of the models made. Sometimes when one of our students makes a mistake, we describe it as a new variation. The Frog base provides flaps for different types of limbs. The body part can be modified. Readers can examine other models to see if parts can be made into a Bird base. We have shown this for the King David Crown.

This last chapter of our first **Origami with Explanations** book. We hope that it has inspired you to continue folding and sharing origami and that the explanations have been helpful and fun. Our *Resources* page provides ideas and links AND you can check out our second book, **More Origami with Explanations**. It has action models, models made from paper currency (tested using US dollar bills, and please try using money from other countries), modular/unit origami, and a peek at fold-and-one-snip models.

The first chapter in **More Origami with Explanations** features the Kissy Fish, an action model By Fritz Jacquet. Note: it is not made from the Fish base. It does provide us an excuse to discuss dividing an edge into thirds and doing a sink fold.

Exercises and Explorations

1. Research the history of the traditional frog.
2. Research the reasoning given for the large number of origami frogs.
3. Do research and teach yourself another frog model.
4. If you do decide to make a small version of this model and want to put it on a lily pad, you will need to calculate the final dimensions of the lily pad and work

backwards to start with an appropriate size of napkin. We don't know if frogs share lily pads.

5. Since you now have seen the Fish base, look up the Whale!
6. Think about combining multiple Kite bases in different ways. Make the drawing and then see if you can fold what you designed. Then think about using the flaps to form different shapes.
7. See #6. See what you can do with multiple Fish bases.
8. The folding procedure for the lily pad may be familiar to you. In Jeanine's family, this was called a Nose Catcher. It also is called a Fortune Teller. Make it with regular paper and see if you can discover or remember the action and discover or remember how messages were written under the flaps to serve as predictions.

Resources
(A listing of places to start your explorations)

OrigamiUSA (https://origamiusa.org/)

OrigamiUSA has listings for organizations around the world, local groups, and conferences as well as a store, called **The Source**, and online classes and workshops.

Books

Peter Engel, **Origami from Angelfish to Zen** + others.

Tomoko Fuse, **Origami Boxes** + others in English and in Japanese.

Gay Merrill Gross, **The Art of Paper Folding** + others.

Rona Gurkewitz and Bennett Arnstein, **Beginner's Book of Modular Origami Polyhedra: The Platonic Solids** + others.

Thomas Hull, **Project Origami: Activities for Exploring Mathematics**, 2nd edition, + others.

Robert Lang, **Twists, Tilings, and Tessellations: Mathematical Methods for Geometric Origami** + others.

John Montroll, **Origami and Math: Simple to Complex** + others.

Robert Neale and Thomas Hull, **Origami Plain and Simple**.

Jeremy Shafer, **Origami to Astonish and Amuse** + others.

Lewis Simon, Bennett Arnstein and Rona Gurkewitz, **Modular Origami Polyhedra**.

Websites (variety of personal websites, services, articles, programs, YouTube channels):

Gilad's Origami Website, *https://www.giladorigami.com/*.
Note: you can use this site to find designers of models and places to find instructions.

Sara Adams, *https://www.happyfolding.com/*.

Erik Demaine, *https://erikdemaine.org/*.

Miri Golan, *https://origametria.com/*.
A well-researched kindergarten and elementary school program

Thomas Hull, *http://origametry.net/*.

Paul Jackson, *http://www.origami-artist.com/*.

Beth Johnson, *http://bethjohnsonorigami.com/*.

Robert Lang, *https://langorigami.com/*.

David Mitchell, *http://www.origamiheaven.com/*.

Jeannine Mosely, *The Connective Power of Origami* by Davie Trueblood, *Technology Review*, August 18, 2015, *https://www.technologyreview.com/s/540661/jeannine-mosely-sm-79-ee-80-phd-84/*.

Jo Nakashima, *https://jonakashima.com.br/*.

Jeremy Shafer, *https://www.youtube.com/jeremyshaferorigami*.

Index

CPSIA information can be obtained
at www.ICGtesting.com
Printed in the USA
LVHW060806211122
733502LV00002B/14